"DON'T TAKE ME THE LONG WAY"

30 TRUE, TRULY OUTRAGEOUS CAB STORIES

M.C. Mars

OFF D EDGE PRESS
SAN FRANCISCO

OFF D EDGE PRESS, 588 Sutter Street, Box 132, San Francisco, CA 94108
www.mcmars.net

The stories "Bob, the Fertilizer Salesman," "'Do You Believe in Jesus?' He Said," "The Death (and Rebirth) of a...," "TV Humor," "Cab Driving 101: Introduction to Abuse," "Daly City Runner," "The Ride" and "Hatred" appeared first in *Showcase Magazine.*

The story "Blood" appeared first in *A&U Magazine.*

Cover design: CP Design
Interior design: Patty Holden

Mars, M. C.
Don't take me the long way / M.C. Mars.—1st ed.
p. cm.
Includes bibliographical references.
ISBN 978-0-9760788-0-7
1. Mars, M. C.—Anecdotes. 2. Taxicab drivers—California—San Francisco—Anecdotes. 3. Taxicabs—California—San Francisco—Anecdotes. I. Title.

PN6268.T3M37 2005 388.4'13214'097946
QBI04-200444

Third Edition
Printed in the United States of America
10 9 8 7 6 5 4 3 2

This book is dedicated to
the memory of William Ball...
mentor/teacher/and friend

WARNING

This may seem presumptuous of me, but if your reading habits resemble mine, you'll start this book of short stories in the middle, opening the book haphazardly and beginning to read wherever. As the writer of this book, I beseech you:

DO NOT DO THIS!!

I started this project back in 1998, almost seven years ago, and one of the main reasons it took me so long to write this thing was trying to figure out the best way to deliver these stories to you, the reader. The structure is that of a pyramid, an equilateral triangle, each side (section) composed of ten stories. There is a rhythm and cadence to these stories that delivers a payoff when read in sequence. I finally got it right. So please, let the dominoes fall the way I set them up, and read the stories in order.

Still, if you're like me, this notice is a big waste of time. You've already skipped this section.

I DRIVE A CAB IN THE CITY BY THE BAAAY

DANGER IS THE WAY I EARN MY PAY

I DRIVE A CAB IN THE CITY BY THE BAAAY

DANGER IS THE WAY I EARN MY PAY

THESE ARE THE DAYS OF THE OUTLAW

NEVER KNOWIN' WHAT U IN FOR

DAYS OF THE OUTLAW

NEVER KNOWIN' WHAT U IN FOR

Contents

Introduction 9

1. The Street Will Eat You Alive

Bob, the Fertilizer Salesman 19
"Do You Believe in Jesus?" He Said 26
The Death (and Rebirth) of a 34
TV Humor. 37
Cab Driving 101: Introduction to Abuse 39
Daly City Runner 43
How I Learned to Drive 48
Red Rover Taxi. 51
A Few Sufficiently Interesting Dispatchers & Fairway Louie 59
The Ride 63

2. Kiss My Rear Axle

Sometimes the Nicest People Can Kill You 79
Sex in a Taxi. 88
This Ain't Nothin' Nice. 91
Hatred. 97
Cab Driving is an Addiction 103
Cab Lot-Camelot/SFO 106
Lusty Lady Jam. 111
The Cadillac of Penis Pumps 115
My Gym Bag 120
Some People Don't Deserve a Cab. 125

3. The Tao of 4 Doors to the Wind

Cab Driving is a Video Game 143
Blood. 146
Moola Metaphysics, or the Bacon Booster 155
MTV Writer Chick 163
Super Geriatric Antediluvian Funk 169
Makin' It with My Muse 176
Tienes la Roca 178
Droppin' Mad Flava with George 187
The Envelope 196
Cab Driving is a Noble Profession 199

Acknowledgments 203

Introduction

An estimated three million people ride taxicabs in America every day. In my twenty-plus years of cab driving, I've probably met close to 200,000 people. And I've talked to many of them one-on-one, sometimes at great length in serious conversations. I've met people from all walks of life, across the whole spectrum of human affairs. Most have been solid, regular, everyday people. Some have had a great sense of humor. Some were assholes. A few were predators. One was a stone-cold killer.

Tourists say, "You should write a book." Party people say, "Tell us your craziest story!" Okay, that's what I'm gonna do, tell you some crazy stories. But be warned. This is a book for adults. Reading these stories, you'll learn things about my life in the street that some of you will find repulsive. You'll learn things about me that my ego would rather not have you know. Secrets, confessions, sordid details...I'll share these with you the way the Buddha, in one of his incarnations, offered his severed carotid artery to a starving Bengal tiger, feeding him on his own blood, so that the tiger might live. I'll lend you my eyes and take you on a trip across four decades, examining life in the inner city.

We'll start off in the suburbs of New York—and using my cab like a starcraft, we'll beam ourselves into a South Bronx ghetto with a couple of pimps. But most of our time will be spent in San Francisco. Beginning in 1981, I'll take you right up to the present moment. In these pages, you'll see things that every cab driver goes through—universals that transcend any particular city or country. The dance of the bottom feeders, fighting over crumbs... The dazzling jabs of enlightenment, amid the stress and flashpoint rage of a city street...The lotus flower of true selfhood, floating up to the level of insight, like a miracle in this Darwinian swamp...

Driving a cab teaches you how to read people. Without trying you become a forensics expert, reading clothing, mannerisms, speech, dialect and *luggage.* Even a Marxist cab driver cannot resist the spell of Gucci luggage. It screams money. And that's what you are out here doing: making money. As a byproduct, you come to see yourself starkly. Your actions are reflected back at you in the behavior of others. The street holds a mirror up to your life. Negative emotions boomerang back, vicious and ugly. And that's why for me, some cab rides are like parables, yielding nuggets of wisdom. Of course, not every cab driver will agree. Some will say, "Kill that noise...It's all about makin' that scratch, that blood money, them crumpled up bills, bro..." Others will say, "It ain't a bad job. Ya got freedom. Nobody looking over your shoulder tellin' you what to do..." For me the best part of the job is the element of unpredictability, never knowing what's gonna happen next. That can also be the worst part.

Hello, are you still with me? Don't be put off by what you think is New Age drivel. This shit is real. I live it. I use these concepts in the street to anticipate outcomes. Without a philosophical mooring the street will eat you alive. And my practice of Buddhism, with its emphasis on causality, has helped me out of some pretty hairy situations. In "Siddhartha," Hermann Hesse says, "It pleases me and seems right that what is of value and wisdom to one man seems nonsense to another." Everything is linked in an intricate web. All human affairs are linked. Every human being on this planet is engaged in a struggle to survive. From CEOs, to scientists, to soldiers, to cab drivers, to the guy in the median strip in a wheelchair with no legs holding up a sign—

everyone is chasing paper. In a cold world, money is insulation. Everyone needs it. In this society—power, influence, respect and opportunity are conditions of wealth.

For a cab driver making peanuts, one of the first things you're challenged with is keeping your self-esteem intact. A cab driver may have been a doctor in India or a tank commander in Iran, but now he's a guy who gets suspicious looks from hotel security when he uses their bathroom. In fact, some guys don't even bother. They just piss in a jar. And nobody's perfect—which means sometimes they miss and wind up urinating on their hands or their clothes, or even in the cab.

Which brings me to the title, "Don't Take Me the Long Way!" Why do people say that? Don't they know it's offensive, suggesting imminent wrongdoing on the part of someone they've just met, and with whom they've entered into a business agreement? And don't they know that just by saying, "Don't Take Me the Long Way," they're telling you they don't have a fucking clue and they're completely at your mercy! Try this same psychology on your dentist, or the contractor you're thinking of hiring to redo your patio, or your auto mechanic—I bet you'll learn to hold your tongue next time.

Hey, Reader—you're gonna ride shotgun. So imagine your cab broke down and you just got towed in. The tow-truck driver is having the worst day of his life and he feels like sharing. "You abandoned your cab. You know you're not suppose to abandon your fucking cab."

"I went to a phone booth. How else was I supposed to call?"

"Get a cellphone."

Now you're back in the garage. Back to square one. The cashier is sending you out in a spare. Spare cabs are all they have left. But the spare he gave you doesn't have any brakes, so you have to find a mechanic and have him install new ones. But all the mechanics are busy—doing repairs, changing brakes, painting. They don't wanna have anything to do with you. So you've gotta go into your pocket and give one of these guys a few bucks. The cab company in its generosity is going to let you work an extra two hours for the two hours you lost waiting for the tow. Meaning, it's going to be a thirteen-hour day. But let's not worry about that. For now, let's find a mechanic. Some guy says, "I'll do you next. Right after I finish here." Cool. Lets hope it doesn't take too long. By the time you get back out on the street, business will be gone....

Hey, Reader—you gotta stop thinking like that. Stay positive. Focus on what's right in front of you—lots of banging and grinding, stacks of parts and gutted wrecks. A radio tucked away somewhere is playing music, King Crimson. Everything you touch is greasy. So don't touch anything. Not the handcarts, the corroded drums, the dead engines, the tires piled high to the ceiling—nothing! Just silently encourage the mechanic to do his shit quickly and don't trip over anything. Watch out for loose tools and shop lights, dangling from the underbellies of jacked-up cabs...

The only reason I brought you here was to show you the power of your own mind. Men fall asleep here. Men become hypnotized by depression in this exhausted light. Dreams disintegrate here. Souls fall through the cracks like white dust going nowhere...

You're standing at the cashier's window at the end of your shift, queued up behind three other drivers waiting to pay. You're so tired you can barely carry on a conversation. Your brain is fried. You've counted your money three or four times to make sure you got it right. After eleven hours of driving that's how it is. Out of 30 rides, 27 or 28 are a blur. But now it's over. You're done. In your hand is your waybill[1] folded in two. Sandwiched between the folds of paper are the company's medallion and the company's money, in the form of cash, charges and para-transit scrip you accumulated during the shift. This money comprises the gates, the gas and the in-house tip, a crucial element in getting the dispatcher's ear. At a nearby table, two Tunisian drivers are having a conversation.

#1: "Omar is very smart."

#2: "No, he's not. If he's smart, he's not driving a cab!"

It's an entry-level job. Immigrants do it. People without verbal skills, who don't have a lot of choices, drive a cab. So does anyone else who doesn't want to be straitjacketed by a suit or have anything to do with a conventional life.

In San Francisco, to drive a cab you must be a licensed California driver and have earned a special cab license called an A-Card. To get an A-Card you must be fingerprinted by the SFPD, and take a written test designed to measure your knowledge of the city. When I took my test, the proctor left the room for about twenty minutes, long enough for the smartest guy there to roll down the map of San Francisco hanging on the wall and call out the answers. Without his help, I know I wouldn't have passed.

These are all true stories. In some cases, the names have been changed to keep me from getting sued.

---

[1]A waybill, or trip sheet, is a record of all your rides for that shift. The police department mandates this.

1

THE STREET WILL EAT YOU ALIVE

"We can only control the end
by making a choice at each step."

—PHILIP K. DICK

Fatal Workplace Injuries

Bureau of Labor Statistics / U.S. Dept. of Labor

DEATHS PER 100,000 WORKERS[2]

	POLICE & DETECTIVES	CAB DRIVERS & CHAUFFEURS
1998	11.6	30.0
1999	11.0	27.3
2000	12.1	25.0
2001	13.5	20.3

[2] Most recent statistics available

Bob, the Fertilizer Salesman

"Everything's got a moral, if you can only find it."
—LEWIS CARROLL

Picked up a guy named Bob. A fertilizer salesman from Florida. He looked like a fertilizer salesman. In a police lineup, you'd pick him out right away as the shit man in the bunch, the entrepreneur of manure. Anyway, Bob wanted a hooker, an ugly hooker, the ugliest one out there.

"Why do you want an ugly hooker?" I asked. His reason was fiscal, not physical—he didn't want to spend a lot of money.

"How much you wanna spend?"

"Twenty, thirty...tops." I looked to see if he was kidding.

He wasn't.

"Bob, Bob, Bob, this is San Francisco...Not in your wildest dreams—a blowjob for thirty bucks? You may get the hooker to put the condom on for thirty bucks, but you're gonna have to suck your own dick." Bob told me he'd give me a bonus, if I could deliver him a hummer under budget.

Guys like Bob—with their almost virginal innocence and endless curiosity about common, everyday things—are a royal pain-in-the-ass. First, they want to buddy-up and know your name. I said Alrick, the most outlandish name that came to mind. And then I cut to the chase. "Okay, Bob, before we start talking money—let's set the ground rules...Let's get this straight.

You, Bob, want me, Alrick, to go out and find you a hooker, is that right?"

"Yes sir," Bob said.

"Okay, well, if you want me to get you a hooker, you're gonna have to pay a pandering fee. That's standard." I had turned fully around and was looking him square in the eyes. He had on a maroon sports jacket and a matching tie and, fittingly, he was short and dumpy and losing his hair.

"A pandering fee?" Bob said, with something akin to wonder in his voice.

"Yeah, a pandering fee. I know a driver who got busted for soliciting a prostitute and it wasn't pretty. I'm risking my ass, putting my cab license on the line."

"How much is the pandering fee?" Bob said squinting at me. I already had him using my jargon—that was good.

"Fifty bucks, fifty on top of the meter."

"Well, I don't know..."

"Look, if I were you, I wouldn't do it. That's ridiculous. You want a $20 hooker and you're gonna shell out fifty for the standard San Francisco pandering fee? C'mon Bob, wake up! Smell the coffee." I kept saying *standard,* drumming it into him.

"Well, ugh, I do wanna...hooker."

"What if I get you a fine one for thirty bucks? Would that be a problem? I mean, it's not going to happen. But if it did, would that present a problem?"

"It would not," Bob said, blowing his nose in a hanky. "Hell, Alrick, I'm easy. Just make damn sure she's a real woman. I'm not in town for the sausage fest..."

I wanted to get rid of this guy. Send him back to the taters and the gators. "Look," I said, "I'm busy right now. I don't have time to go bargain hunting for hookers." It was a slow mid-week night and I definitely wasn't busy. But people like Bob get in the cab and drain you with their unquenchable stupidity. It's like they put a straw in your head and suck out all the juice. "Either you're gonna pay me the $50 pandering fee, now, up front, or you're gonna have to leave," I said, in no uncertain terms.

Bob reached into his pocket and pulled out some bills, but not enough. So we went to an ATM and he paid the balance on his pandering fee. Now I was happy and relaxed.

"You're guaranteeing that you're gonna find me a hooker, right?" Bob said. "Or my money back? Are we on the same page, Alrick?"

"Bob, if I don't find you a hooker, and a truly vile, repulsive wench at that, I'm gonna turn myself in to the Better Business Bureau for fraud. Believe me, pal, I'm going the extra mile. She's not gonna have a tooth in her head."

"Gum me till I come..." said Bob, sounding more aggressive.

So off we went, ogling for ugly, scouring for skuzz. I figured we'd hit Capp Street first for a warm-up. I had an intuition that Bob was gonna fuck up the first connection, so I wanted to hold something back. And, as it turned out, I was 100% correct. Almost instantly upon our arrival at Capp Street, I found Bob a skinny white chick in fishnets with tattoos on her arms and bruises on her neck. It was miserably cold and she didn't even have a jacket on. You felt sorry for her, until you saw that predatory look in her eye. I honked and waved her over to the cab. She came up to the window, but didn't want to get inside. Who could blame her? If I was a hoe, I'd want to see what I was getting into.

I once had a Mexican girl tell me that, when she was working in Albuquerque, some cowboys kidnapped her, hit her over the head with a hammer and left her for dead. "I can appreciate the caution," I told her.

"But look at this nice man," I said, gesturing towards Bob. "All he wants is a blow job…And it would probably be safer, in terms of being observed by the police, if you got in *NOW!!* I'll drive around the block. You guys negotiate."

She got in. Said she'd take forty, but Bob had to pay for the room. Bob said, "I know you have a room. You're just gonna pocket the extra money." The girl insisted she didn't have a room. "You have to have a room," Bob said, "How else can you do business. You have to take your johns someplace…" But the girl said no. She didn't work that way. She pointed to a little dark niche in the alley and said, "We'll do it back there." Bob laughed and said, "You probably have your friends back there waiting to jump me."

The woman said, without a false note in her voice, "Mister, if I had any friends, do you think I'd be out here in this cold, freezin' my ass off, sucking dick?"

One has to respect such impeccable logic. She huffed and got out, slammed the door and walked away. "Guess we fudged that one," Bob said.

"What do you mean, fudged?"

"We blew it," Bob said.

This was going to be more difficult than I'd originally thought. However, I wasn't about to lose my pandering fee, so I pulled out my big guns and took him over to Octavia Street under the elevated freeway, where the crackheads hang.

Right away, we found this pathetic, toothless, crack monster, fifty years old, hair like brillo, enormous pendulous tits, beady red eyes poppin' out of her head. She was standing in the dim glow of a malfunctioning streetlight.

"There's your girl," I said.

"Nasty as hell…" Bob said.

"Well, that's what you wanted, wasn't it?"

"Okay, ugh—yeah…Is she white, or black? It's hard to see in this light."

"Look, Bob, I can't drive around with you all night, even though the meter's running."

"Don't worry. I've got plenty of money, Alrick."

"I am worrying Bob. This is the shot. Don't blow it. Lemme do the talking."

The hooker came over to the cab and jumped right in. She had on an X-large T-shirt over her sweater. It was black and patterned with all these puckered, pink, kissy lips and in bold letters across the front, it said, *Mister Ass.* "I like your tee-shirt," Bob said.

Inside, she started doing this weird thing with her mouth and told us she was "tweekin'." Then she opened her purse and pulled out a brown bottle of hydrogen peroxide. She took a swig and swished it around in her mouth before opening the door, leaning over and spitting it out.

"Very hygienic…What was that all about?" Bob said interrogating the hoe.

"He wants a blow job for twenty bucks…" I prompted.

"Do you have a room?" Bob interrupted, while the concept was still forming like a mist on the frontal lobe of her brain.

"C'mon, Bob…Don't start this shit again."

"I don't know whether I want to pay $20 for *her,*" Bob said. The woman was virtually in another galaxy and seemed not in the least bit offended by these remarks.

"You said twenty bucks," I reminded Bob. "Actually, you said thirty. So I'm getting you a deal."

The woman watched us dicker. She asked for a cigarette. We ignored her.

"I changed my mind," Bob said. "I don't wanna pay twenty dollars. I wanna pay ten." As if awakened from a dream, the hooker said, "Okay, I'll take ten dollars."

But Bob said, "No, make it five. Five dollars." She looked over at me for support and she said to Bob, "You said ten."

"Well, I changed my mind. I want it for five."

"Why not go for three?" I said. "Let's have a white flower day sale, go for three!" I handed the woman a dollar and said, "Here's a down payment. You get the rest when the job is done." By now Bob and I were convulsed with laughter, tears were running down our faces. Even the hooker was smiling.

"Do I hear seventy-five cents?" Bob said. "Seventy-five cents and a cigarette?"

The woman appeared utterly baffled. I told her she had to leave. She said, "I wanna hire this cab."

"Sure thing," Bob chuckled. "Y'know, Alrick, how bout we forget the whole thing. I'll pay you and that's that."

"I wanna rent this cab," the battered hooker said.

"No, hon, we go…You stay. I mean, we stay, you go…" Bob yuck-yucked, and reached across her lap and pushed open her door. The interior light came on, dimly illuminating the faces.

"Have a nice night…" Bob said, showing her the half-open door with a broad sweep of his arm.

"Muthafucka!!!" The hooker growled, and kicked hard at the door with her sizable heel. "You think this a joke? Huh, white boy!!!"

"Whoa…" Bob said, snapping to attention. "Where did that come from?"

Her face became a mask of indignation. "What you thinkin'? This dumb bitch…She a hoe. She addicted to crack. She been in and out of institutions all her life. She a rug…We can walk all over this bitch. *Well, fuck y'all white muthafuckas*...The city took away my kids. Is that funny? I ain't leavin' till I gets paid!!

"Paid for what?" I said.

"For puttin' up with yo' stupid ass."

"Ah, shit..." Bob said, reaching into his pocket. "White man's guilt." He gave her five bucks.

"That's half of it...," she said.

"That's all of it," Bob said.

After a long and painful standoff, I coughed up the other five. Afterwards, at the hotel when we totaled the damage, this extortion money was added to Bob's bill.

"Do You Believe in Jesus?" He Said

It was a bleak Saturday night, sliding into Sunday, just after 3:00 A.M. The country was in a recession. San Francisco, a year after the Loma Prieta earthquake, was in a depression, suffering from severe tourist-drought and the scourge of AIDS.

I took an order in the Richmond District at 22nd & Geary. The house was dark, a rickety Victorian, built of wood. The door, located atop a high staircase, was partly hidden by a mass of untended shrubbery. I shut off the engine, but left my headlights on in the deserted street. I climbed the creaky stairs cautiously to ring the bell. No telling who was lurking in the shadows.

A husky guy comes out. I'd estimate him to be in his mid-30s, wearing a Harley vest with a motorcycle helmet tucked under his arm.

"Too fucked up to ride," he says, and throws himself into the back. He gives me an address. "I'll show you. It's a dead-end street, right next to the golf course."

"How's your night been?" I ask.

"Weird, very fucking weird. Some real strange shit just went down." I stole a glance in the mirror. Is he drunk? If he's too drunk there's no sense making conversation.

"What happened?"

"I'm still thinking it over, man."

I let him think.

At this late hour, only a few cars were on the road—mostly empty cabs, racing down Geary Blvd for twenty or thirty blocks, vying and jockeying for position on the off chance that a warm body would pop up out of nowhere and flag the winner. Hungry dogs fighting for meat, that's how my dispatcher puts it.

"You know how sometimes a thing gets totally out of hand?" my passenger mused.

"Yeah...," I said.

"My best friend just kicked me out his house."

"Why'd he do that? "

"He says I made a pass at his mom." He shook his helmet in his hands like he was mixing a martini. "We been drinkin' since this morning."

"Did you...make a pass at his mom?" I asked, adjusting the mirror to check him out. He rolled down his window and a blast of cold air chopped me in the neck. At the stop light the cab to my left, not seeing I had a passenger, was gung ho to beat me off the line.

"Can I smoke?"

"It's a no-smoking cab."

"I can deal with that. But we gotta stop some place soon, so I can buy smokes."

"Sure. Now, back to the story. Your best friend accused you of hittin' on his mom?"

"Dawg!!! She was hitting on me!" He snapped opened the visor of his helmet, and then slapped it shut. "Takes two to tango—right?"

"Was his mom drunk?"

"Sloshed! I was doin' body shots off her big tits. And for a woman her age, the broad looks damn good."

"Where was your buddy, while this was happenin'?"

"He was in front of the TV in the back room, passed out on the sofa. Then he woke his dumb-ass up and came in the kitchen for a beer. That's when he caught us."

He put his helmet on—a quarterback listening for the next play to be signaled in. Then he took it off.

"And you know what's so fucked up about all this? The lady's beautiful. She looks like Sophia Loren with those big, pouty lips."

"That could be trouble."

"She gave me her phone number at work. She wants me to call her. Her son is my best friend, man! If you were me, what would you do?"

"Me?" I said, zipping down 19th Avenue, past ghostly gas stations and segmented rows of boxy little houses. "I'd get your cigarettes at Zim's."

"No, homie, for real. People are bastards. You can't trust nobody nowadays." He made a little tittering noise. "I can't even trust my own damn self." I looked at him and he fixed me with a hi-beam stare. "Do you believe in Jesus?" he said, transforming himself in a flash, into a wild-eyed, Bible-thumping evangelist. It was as if I had sat on the remote and accidentally changed the channel. "I do," he said. "Make no bones about it. I do."

"Here we are!" I yelled, screeching to a halt in the bus stop at 19th and Taraval.

He didn't budge. "It's a simple question and I would appreciate an answer. Do you believe in salvation through Christ?"

"Lemme answer you this way. I believe our time on earth is limited and we have to make the most of it. And that's doubly true for your time in this cab. So please, get your cigarettes…"

"I believe each and every one of us has to make a choice. Do you choose Satan or do you choose God? Ain't no sitting on the fence. Romans 14:12, 'They will have to stand before God and give an account.'"

"Brother, please..." I reached over and opened his door, pointing toward the bright radiance of Zim's, the Promised Land of coffee and cigarettes. He walked away grumbling and didn't bother to close his door.

After a certain number of strange incidents like this, a cab driver develops nerves of steel and a bedrock patience that can only be moved by the most seismic stupidities. Without these survival skills, one could easily go bananas and turn into a Travis Bickle. But watching this idiot inside Zim's, staring at the cigarette machine like it was the monolith in Kubrick's movie "A Space Odyssey 2001"—who wouldn't get upset?

So I go inside the greasy spoon shrine to Elvis, with the late-night drunks and the candy-apple upholstery that squeaks and crunches when you sit on it.

"What's up?" I said. "You've been in here for like ten minutes."

He ignored me, dropping in one coin at a time, all of them nose-diving through the alimentary canal of the machine, *clink-clink-clink*, voided and rejected. Finally, after four or five tries, down came the Marlboros and the matches. He flipped me a quick, over-the-shoulder sneer and did a Braille-trail with his hand, to see if there was anything else below.

"Dude, we're done. I can't it take any more. You owe me $12.90. Plus, whatever's on the meter right now."

"I don't owe you shit. When I get to my destination, you get paid."

"As far as I'm concerned, you're at your destination," I said, widening the space between us.

"Get lost," he said, dismissively.

"I'm not going anywhere, until you pay me."

He put on his helmet. Inside the restaurant, heads were turning.

"I said, I ain't payin' you shit!!!" he yelled. And then he took a wild, backhanded swipe in my direction. The little matchbook he held between finger and thumb slipped loose and hit me in the chest, where it ricocheted and landed like a fat moth in a plate of scrambled eggs belonging to a cop (whom neither of us had noticed until now), sitting at the end of the counter.

Looking mystified by the sudden interruption of his breakfast, this fireplug of an Asian cop daintily lifted the matchbook from his eggs and deposited it—like a vital piece of evidence—on a napkin. He then turned around in a slow and deliberate manner, looking first at me and then at the guy wearing his motorcycle helmet inside the restaurant.

"What's going on here?" the cop asked, getting up slowly.

"I'm a cab driver. He owes me money for the ride."

"Yeah, but the ride ain't over," my passenger snarled.

"Yes, it is," I told him.

"Did you ride in his cab?" the cop demanded. The motorcycle/evangelist said nothing, rocking on his feet from side to side.

"I'm talking to you…" the cop growled.

"What??"

"Did you ride in this man's cab?"

"What??"

"Are you deaf!! Take off that helmet and pay the man…"

"Why? He don't wanna take me where I need to go."

"Pay him, or go to jail…" the cop snarled.

"I don't think so," the guy said, flatly.

And that is when the cop lost it. "Get on the floor and put your hands behind your head!" He brought out the bracelets.

Helmet-head took a step forward, as if to run. In a heartbeat, the cop was on him.

"This ain't right!" my passenger cried.

The cop, who only came up to the man's Adam's apple, was trying savagely to force him to the ground. Mouths dropped. Forks froze in mid-bite.

The guy was on his knees, shoved up against the cigarette machine, saying, "Chill, man! Wha'd I do? Wha'd I do?" The guy tried to pull his helmet off, but the cop wouldn't let him. He was in a rage, this cop, pressing and twisting down on the guy's helmet, as if his head were a bottle of ketchup. Trying to preserve the crime scene, I suppose.

"I can't breathe!" the man bellowed.

"Shut up and face the floor!" Saliva frothed in the corners of the cop's mouth. The cuffs went on. And in a flash, his back-up arrived. Five, maybe six squad cars, all in a commotion of sirens and spinning rotor-lights—just like the movies.

The perp was dragged from the restaurant, de-helmeted and stuffed inside a cruiser. He glared at me with great hatred in his eyes. The cop saw this, and said, "I don't think he's gonna get you anything for Christmas."

"That guy is high on something."

"Follow us back to the station. I'll get you your money."

At the station, the arresting officer introduced me to the sergeant on duty, the stereotype of a gruff, Irish cop. As the officer gave his account, I couldn't believe what I was hearing. His spin made the matchbook sound like a deadly weapon. And even though I wanted nothing more than to get paid and split, in the interests of a higher justice, I felt I had to clear up a few things—a mistake that landed me in constabulary quicksand.

"Pull this guy's medallion. He doesn't wanna cooperate. He's not going anywhere," the desk sergeant said, slamming his fist down furiously.

I looked at my watch. I have less than an hour left in the shift. If I'm late, the company hits me with a stiff fine, a late fee. But the real heart-stopper is the confiscated medallion. Without a medallion, the cab can't go out on the street. At two and a half shifts per day, this adds up to a whole helluva lot of money (anywhere from $250 to $300), for which I am solely responsible.

The night was taking on Kafkaesque proportions. The Asian cop had me follow him into a bare, cold, little cell-of-a-room. He sat behind a desk taking notes.

"You said he was using drugs...Is that correct?"

"No, I said, 'He must be high on something.' I can't say for sure that he was using drugs."

"What can you say *for sure* then? In the restaurant, you told me he was high on drugs."

"I said, 'I think he's high on drugs.' It was a supposition, officer..." *Supposition* was the first word that came out my mouth. I couldn't think of anything simpler.

"What's a supposition?" The cop said.

"A guess...a theory..."

He was writing all this down. "I'm not impressed with fifty-dollar words. How do you spell *supposition?*"

"I'm dyslexic. I can't spell. I'll have to write it down for you." There was a pause, eye contact, suspicion. "Can I borrow some paper and a pen?" He tore off a piece of paper and handed me his pen. I wrote it down. He studied it.

"So you never actually saw him using drugs, is that correct?"

Yes, it is, officer. But I can also say the guy was acting very weird. You saw him...in the restaurant."

Just when I thought it looked very bad—very, very bad—as if I'd better plan on spending the night, some gofer from the Sergeant's desk burst in, and said, "Forget it. Let him go. The guy's got a star. We found a star in his wallet."

My passenger—incredibly—was a cop! And just like that, in one fell swoop of damage control, everything was swept under the rug. I got my medallion back and my marching orders. And under the watchful eye of a female officer, the contents of the man's pockets were spread out before me on a table. I was paid the $12.90 he owed me. She handed me a ten and a five and, before I could even blink, she said, "Where's his change? He gets back change."

I felt like saying, "What, no tip?" But I thought better of it and fished in my pocket for the coins.

The Death (and Rebirth) of a...

The death of a cab driver is a footnote, buried in the back of the paper. As news goes, it's a non-event. No presidential cortege, no honor guard, no flag-draped coffin, no clattering hooves down Pennsylvania Avenue, no somber, twenty-one gun salute. For me, it would have been a two-inch blurb in the police blotter and some gossip, lasting a few weeks around the garage.

In San Francisco, Plexiglas shields—the standard protection for the driver against attack—rarely exist. Often the first observation a stranger to San Francisco makes is, "How come you guys don't have those screens?"

When I tell them how much we hate them, because of how they're installed, because they create a major barrier to communication, because passengers complain about leg room, because they further alienate us—who feel alone and isolated to begin with—by putting us in an enclosed space resembling a terrarium... ("*Let's watch rat-driver climb on his wheel...*") and judging by their look, the stranger still seems unconvinced, I say, "Hey, this is San Francisco, the city of openness and free love and yadee-yadah..."

To which they reply, "Yeah, but this is your life you're talking about..."

~

I made a tourniquet with my hanky. I checked my watch. It was 8:17. Eleven minutes had elapsed since the attack. The hanky wasn't working. It was too small and kept slipping off, so I tore my shirt and used it instead. Dark, plum-colored blood trickled down my fingers. As I started towards the overpass, I thought about my lack of medical insurance. I thought about the mysterious inter-relatedness of events—how a dangerous blowout last month on 101 and my subsequent march through the brush of the freeway to find a phone had prepared me for this, so that I was familiar with the lay of the land and wouldn't lose time and waste blood—I knew exactly where to go. At the overpass, there would be a cyclone fence that was easy to climb, even with one hand.

I walked through deserted streets, waving at cars that never stopped. I headed down a paved road into the giant parking lot of City College. It was empty, except for a beat-up Volvo. A young mother and her grade-school daughter were turning in a semicircle to leave. I could have run up to them and asked for help, but I didn't want to inflict my drama on these two innocents.

I went another 500 yards to the 76 station at Ocean & Phelan, where the attendant—a small, simian-like man in the tight confinement of his booth—stared at me idiotically, refusing to call 911. To get back at him, I wiped blood across his window and growled, "I'm a cab driver! I've been stabbed!"

The taxicab is a laboratory for human development. The street is a classroom where all emotions and desires are on display. Some passengers, total strangers, are so incredibly kind and caring, they enter the cab bearing plates of food to feed the driver on Thanksgiving and Christmas. Others just give you big tips and wish you a safe night. Still others, in their fierce eccentricity, show a remarkable degree of sensitivity, like the bare-assed paladin in leather chaps who brought his own towel to sit on during the Folsom Street Fair. And some people, some people don't have a friggin' clue!!!

"*WHAT COMES AROUND, GOES AROUND*" is the highest metaphysical law of the street and, for that matter, on the planet. And though I believe this with my deepest conviction, it took me a long time—and a long line of disasters, setbacks, and defeats—to grasp this in its strict dynamics. On the molecular level of the street, where cause and effect spin around faster than in other work environments, you often pay for slick, slippery moves with your life. Seeing this as a possible end for myself, I became a student of karma, realizing that honesty is not so much "the best policy" as it is a necessary and essential survival technique.

Much as reading books and thinking critically develops the intellect, cab driving develops the intuition. Richard Wilhelm, the great scholar of the I Ching, says, "Real intuition is in accord with logic, only it transcends logic."

In the street, you trust your gut. Second thoughts can cost you dearly. For example, I called in all my karma chits that day, on September 24, 1995, when my passenger threw a garrote over my head, put a box cutter to my neck and, through clenched teeth, yelled in my ear, "Drive, muthafucka, or I'll kill you..."

TV Humor

If every human being on earth is, as they say, a unique creation, then transvestites also run the full range of types. Some are intellectual and quiet, some are rambunctious and brainless, some are hookers, some are librarians, some are kind, some are funny, and some are cruel. But I have noticed that the trappings, if not the more mysterious intangibles of womanhood, obsess them all.

The one who got into my cab at the Cow Palace after The Rodeo looked like a limp penis in a cowboy hat. She accused me of taking her the long way, which, as you know, I always resent, then bluntly rejected my route by her comparison of other routes, which would have consigned us to the hell of gridlock for at least forty-five minutes to an hour. She was Hispanic and, owing to her sketchy English and her certainty that every cab driver was a crook-on-wheels, my arguments failed to convince her. By the time we reached her seedy hotel on 6th Street, where she paid and brayed and stiffed me, the trading of insults had reached the high watermark.

"You're telling me I don't know shit?" I said. "I know this: You're not a real woman!"

With intent, I had smashed the glass display case of her self-image. Expecting anything to follow—violence, a stiletto heel aimed at my head, maybe even the swipe of a knife, I reached under the seat for my weapon.

"Jes, I am woman," she spat back.

"No, you're not!"

And after several dumb rounds of "Jes-I-am."

"No-you're-not."

"Jes I am!" "No you're not!" I said, "Then prove it. Show me your pussy!"

At which point, up goes the dress, down go the panties, and there—exposed on the nasty vinyl of my taxi—was the happy nappy of a manicured pussy. She looked at me with the vapid allure of a *Penthouse* centerfold and said, "See, you piece-of-shit-mother-fucker..."

"See what?" I said. "You're a transsexual. No real woman would ever do that!"

Hard cursing and more hi-volume insults outside culminated in a hand-mauling attack on my license plate. She twisted the shit out of it. In the street overflowing with garbage, she merged into an ambulatory group of men hanging in front of a bright storefront. They were selling hubbas (vintage 1990), which some kept balled up in their mouths to swallow in case of cops. I thought of Demosthenes, the Greek orator, who sharpened his articulation by talking with stones in his mouth.

"Break you off sumphen proper, noffin gaffo, noffin janky 'bout my game."

Cab Driving 101: Introduction to Abuse

Our saga begins in New Rochelle, a suburb of NYC. I'm around nine or ten. My little chums and me phony-phone call a cab to our apartment building. When we hear the cab pull up outside, we sneak into the lobby and slide to our bellies, crawling like soldiers to get as close to the front door as possible without being seen. According to plan, the driver is in the entryway, ringing the bell of the neighborhood grouch. We peek out from behind the curtains, waiting for a reaction.

"Cab's here!" The driver singsongs.

"Whad cab? Who called a cab? I didn't call no cab. You woke me up, dammit!"

The driver stands there looking puzzled, muttering swear words. We find this unbelievably hilarious, and twist around on the floor holding our stomachs to stifle the laughter. "Did you see the look on that cab driver's face!"

A couple of years later, we tweak the act and add something extra. Just as he's about to leave, someone jumps outside and whistles, "Taxi!"

The cab grinds to a halt. At which point (depending on the season), we pelt his cab with a hail of water balloons or snowballs—or maybe, on an exotic day, a dozen stolen eggs—and scatter in all directions, hell-bent on a good chase.

These are the kinds of causes that bring bad effects into a young life. Although at the time I was completely ignorant of this, there was a connection that even I could make. My father, Sam Silvan, was a route man in the Bronx, delivering Arnold bread. At least once every winter, he would come home with a story about how some punks had bombarded his truck with snowballs and almost made him crash. At the end of his story, my father would say to me, "What kind of fucking idiot would do such a thing?" And I would stare down at the kitchen table and shake my head.

As an older youth, I'd watch my dad give cab drivers big tips. "Working people are the best tippers," he'd proclaim with pride. But when I got together with my boys and we had a few beers, *bolting* from a taxicab became a minor art form and a source of great delight, as we stood around late at night passing a joint and reliving the excitement of the getaway.

Never—never in my wildest dreams did I imagine that in decades to come, I too would be driving a taxicab.

But there you are, only a few years later behind the wheel of a New Mall Taxi, slogging through traffic on a muggy Sunday evening in August. The Mets game is letting out and the Van Wyck Expressway is a parking lot. The year is 1971. You're twenty, living alone in a boarding house in Pelham, a stone's throw from the Glen Island Casino. You want to be a poet and you just quit college for the second time to study under the sharp eye of the lyrical poet—José Garcia Villa, the protégé of e.e. cummings. Tomorrow night classes will resume at his crowded apartment at 744 Greenwich Street, a place piled high to the ceiling with amazing books.

But that's tomorrow and, right now, you're stewing in traffic, returning from JFK, where you just got a ticket for double-parking. Even with shades on and the visors down, the vermilion disk blazing at eye-level is twisting your optic nerves like a wet towel, and the black interior of the Chevy Caprice holds the heat like a blast furnace. The windows are all down, but so what? It doesn't matter. Nothing helps. The heat is unbearable. And the exhaust from the cars in front of you creates mirages. Let the sweat run down your face and glue you to the seat, you're still not gonna turn on the A/C! Every time you do, these fucking cabs overheat! Like that poor slob up ahead, hood raised blocking traffic.

As you get closer, you can smell the boiling water steaming from his engine and see the green anti-freeze leaking from the car's undercarriage. Inching your way past him, you come bumper-to-bumper with some Puerto Rican gangsters in a stripped-down Bonneville convertible. They cut in front of you, and flip *you* off.

Say what!!?

And of course, you have to look. You can't help it. It's just one of those knee-jerk things you can't help doing. The hot Afro-Cuban rhythms blaring from their radio command attention, and you play right into their hands. There are three of them, mean-looking, with prison tattoos. They're talking shit. It's not easy, but you stare straight ahead and silently grind your teeth.

"Bitch, whatchya gonna do! I'll cold drop kick your ass across town..." says a skinny shirtless kid with tattoos on his neck.

"I'll beat you 'til the brakes come off, bitch," says his partner wearing a silk do-rag.

You let it sink in. You see them out the corner of your eye.

"Muthafucka...I'm talkin' to you."

An ice cream cone probably aimed at your head hits the

windshield like the droppings of a five-hundred-pound pigeon. You reciprocate with the finger.

Again: Marshall, you've fucked up!

Chhaaachoo! Someone spits, and a loogey the size of an oyster dangles like a pendulum from the edge of the door, hanging by a glistening filament, waiting to fall. This is the kinda shit that happens to young cab drivers. Punks challenge you. They wanna yank your chain, and, if you let them and take the bait, it's like quicksand—the more you struggle the faster you go down.

You already had a fight last week with a cab driver over who caused the collision that left both of your side-mirrors dangling. You don't need this. At the next gas station, you find some industrial-strength paper towels, and wipe away the mess. But the humiliation and the pent-up rage—that's another story, part of a larger story...the story of being a cab driver.

Daly City Runner

Rabbits, that's what the old-timer called them. "I had these rabbits take off on me," he'd say, adding with a touch of Stoicism, "comes with the territory..."

"Ever have anyone bolt on you?" an athletic schoolboy in a hockey jersey and his sidekick asked me one night.

"Twice, in twenty years," I said, and dropped my foot on the gas, peeling and swerving through traffic for optimal effect. "Caught 'em both times and prosecuted their ass to the full extent of the law."

Silence.

"You guys have money?" It was a good question.

"Yeah, we got money. Wassup..." The kid flashed some dough. His partner, sitting right behind me, sported a ball cap cocked to one side and mugged random violent faces in my mirror. This alarmed me, until I realized he had a really bad facial tic.

"No disrespect intended, but can I hold some dead presidents?"

He gave me a look and slipped me a twenty. I put the money in my shirt pocket. "Hopefully, my sprinting days are over," I said with a chuckle that fell into an abyss of undiluted silence.

I shouldn't have picked them up. But they caught the door right as the previous passenger was leaving. Still, I was in one of those moods where I felt rather invincible, so the hell with it…

There had been an episode a few years ago, late at night—three dudes flagged me in SOMA at 6th & Folsom. They told me they had been to a club, and now they were calling it a night. The vibe was strange. It was wrong. They were too quiet—huddled together, whispering. I didn't have any protection that night. No pepper spray, no tire-iron under the seat, no super-inflatable-condom to crush them like an airbag, nothing—just my wits and a strong determination to get paid.

We exited at Serramonte and drove down "auto row" in Colma. In an eerie stillness, we drove past lines and lines of stickered cars, new and used, catching the cold light of a polished moon. Then we went into the hills to a remote woodsy area in the middle of nowhere. They had me stop, and when I did, they jetted. Like an idiot, I raced after them. Midway into a eucalyptus grove I stopped, and watched them vanish into thin air.

Walking back to the cab, doors flung wide open, headlights glowing in the foggy mist, I realized the monumental stupidity of what I had just done. How lucky I was to be standing in this dark place unharmed. I looked out over the valley below. The hill fell off precipitously into a pulsing tapestry of light. There wasn't a soul in sight, or a house within a hundred yards of me. The only sound was the faint rustling of the eucalyptus leaves in the wind and the distant whoosh of high-speed traffic the other side of a sound wall.

"Some people can't seem to grasp the fact that I'm out here trying to earn a living," I said to them, looking at Tic-man in the mirror. "I know you think I'm in it for the glory, but you're wrong." Sarcasm, of even the most obvious kind, was wasted on these kids.

"If you had a hooker in here and she looked like Cindy Crawford, would you let her slide, if she offered to polish your knob?"

"A hooker that looked like Cindy Crawford?" I played with the image.

"Yeah...," the kid said, all lit up.

"No," I said, shaking my head. "She'd still have to pay."

"Damn, that's cold-blooded. That's pimpin'!"

"You ride, you pay. This is a business."

"In twenty years, only two people tried to run?"

"That's right." The guy behind me was twitching and jerking, mugging violently.

"You guys know what Karma is? Well, it's bad Karma to bolt from a taxi."

"Only if you believe in that stuff."

"Doesn't matter whether you believe it or not. Ignorance is not without consequences. What comes around goes around. Like the guy who tried to hightail it outta of here—he got, umm, run over by another cab!"

"Fo' sheezy?"

"Yeah. It was ugly."

"Did he get splat?"

"He died, man."

"I thought you said they prosecuted both times."

"They did. First they arrested the sonofabitch. Then he died in custody."

"What happened the other time?" I didn't have to drag this invention out any further. They were distracted by a classic, a 1981 Oldsmobile Ninety-Eight.

"That car is hella tight."

"That car is off-the-hook."

"I'd put a big-ass muffler on that shit."

The other time someone ran was early in my career. It was

Fisherman's Wharf, after midnight. I was cruising Jefferson Street, hoping to find a stranded bartender against the neutron-bomb landscape of a tourist trap without people—muffled boom of foghorns, mannequin windows, hosed-down crab stalls, a pack of raccoons (or rats the size of raccoons) crossing the street in front of me. I heard a whistle and a few blocks away, near Pompeii's Grotto, I saw someone waving. He was jumping up and down, doing jumping jacks to catch my attention. He's white, 5'9", 140 lbs., 19 or 20 years old. A busboy, going home to Daly City, he tells me.

We drove down John Daly Boulevard. It was an unusually clear night without fog. "Left here at Denny's," he said.

I made the turn, cut through the shopping center parking lot and came out the rear onto a narrow street. Midway into the block, he says, "Okay, stop here."

I stop. And zippo—he's gone, a few steps away from the big glass door of a red brick apartment house.

I lit after him, entering the building on his heels before the door, held open by the wind, had time to close. The hallway was shaped like a horseshoe. Filigreed mirrors ran in sections along the walls. I heard him clomping heavily down the carpeted hallway, saw him streak across a mirror and disappear. When he stopped, I heard him breathing, huffing and puffing to catch his breath.

I stood there fingering the coarse texture of the wallpaper. I stood there for what seemed a very long time. He took a few noisy steps, and stopped. I didn't budge. He then faked going one way, and took off in the opposite direction. It was a lame move. Doubling back, I caught him rushing at me, full speed. He dipped, and tried to duck under my outstretched arm. I missed a clean tackle. We bounced off each other, crashed into the wall of trembling reflections, and tumbled to the carpet. I tried to put a headlock on him, but he slipped away and scrambled to his feet. When I got to mine, he had a *shiv* out and was pointing it at me, advancing. I ripped off my leather jacket, wrapped it around my arm and started backpedaling for the door. I hardly had time to consider the fix I was in, when out of nowhere the cavalry showed up in the form of two Daly City cops.

The cops drew their guns and shouted to my passenger to drop the knife. Wisely, he complied. The cops made him sit against the wall, hands on his head. They tugged his arms back to his shoulder blades and put the cuffs on extra tight. When they searched him, they found seventy bucks. He paid his fare.

We were at the end of the ride—me and the two suspect runners—on Diamond Heights Blvd., overlooking the shimmering city.

"Left here on Goldmine. Take us all the way in!" Hockey Shirt said, pointing with his chin down a steep, unlit ramp ending in a cul-de-sac of low-income, Section 8 housing.

"I'll give you your change right here," I said, reaching into my breast pocket for the money.

"Take us all the way in!" the kid boomed in a commanding voice.

I turned and looked him dead in the eye. A hooptie[3] pulled up behind us. His brights blinded us. He honked impatiently.

"Gotta go!" I said.

I looked at his friend sitting directly behind me—his hard eyes and twitching repertoire of violent faces. Then I looked back at him.

For a long time nobody moved…

---

[3]A beat-up, old car

How I Learned to Drive

"It is true: I earn my living.
But believe me, it is only an accident."
—BERTOLT BRECHT

Got a job. Had to...

The ultimatum came down. "No eighteen-year-old son of mine is gonna sleep in my house and eat my food and not cough up a goddamn dime..."

Bla-bla-blah... Yeah, yeah, yeah...

A few days later, I found myself ding-donging deliveries for a pharmacy in Wykagyl called Cherry Hill. My boss was a middle-aged gonif named Milt. He had watery eyes, fishy lips and a head full of shine. He was the kind of boss who would drop everything to show someone how incompetent they were.

"Mister Pepsi Man, no! Don't dump the cases over there like that. Put your soda over here, like this. Make a nice straight line, see?" And after he had shown Mister Pepsi Man, and many others, the error of their ways, he would walk away muttering, "*Schmuck!*" under his breath.

Milt (according to Milt) was *sharp as a tack.* He'd *been around the block a few times.* He knew everything. Except this—the kid he hired to make deliveries did not know how to drive.

I'd passed the drivers test (on the third try) and had a valid New York State driver's license, issued to one Marshall Curtis Silvan, a skinny kid of 5'10" sporting an afro and a skimpy goatee.

Still, my driving skills were not quite up to par. My parents, painfully aware of this, had refused to let me drive their only car, a used '68 Impala. So what was a young cat with no money and no wheels to do? The pharmacy job presented me with the perfect solution—a golden opportunity to practice driving without someone looking over my shoulder, busting my balls at every turn. Early lessons with my father had accomplished nothing except to fill me with rage and self-doubt. The man spat criticism and corrections, as if he were getting paid by the word.

"You almost hit that parked car!" "You almost clipped that guy's mirror!" "You're on the wrong side of the street, moron. And don't slam on the brake, you fucking idiot!"

The scouting reports that came back to my mother were bleak, impossibly negative: I was a cretin. My 14-year-old sister could do better. That's why this pharmacy gig was so cool. I was El Solo. Backseat drivers intimidated me.

In the second week of my new job, Milt—after questioning me about a dent he had never seen before—asked me to drive him to the train station in Scarsdale.

"I'm in a big hurry. I've got seven minutes to catch the 11:10 to Grand Central Station." And as he tossed me the keys to his sky-blue Corvair, he said, "Don't spare the horses."

I wanted to make a good impression. I followed Milt's request to a tee. In a school zone, I even exceeded it by 30 miles per hour.

"Holy buckets! Slow down, you're gonna kill someone."

The car flew around a yellow school bus stopping to make a drop-off. To avoid the shrill-pitched little bodies frolicking near the curb, I flicked the steering wheel first west, then east, then west again in a rapid-fire motion that sent Milt bouncing off the dashboard and the ceiling. He looked gravely ill and leaned out the window, as if he might heave his breakfast. It was a sight I could not resist watching and, in that moment of distraction, the car swerved out of control.

"Eyes on the road!" Milt screamed, as he belched with acid indigestion. "Stop the car right here, right now. Just stop."

On command, my foot hit the brake and Milt's forehead smashed against the windshield. Thwack! A thick welt and a massive cut appeared. Snorting air out his nose, he bled like a pig. The repulsive noise that emitted from his throat was midway between a death gurgle and a giggle. I observed this spectacle with a mixture of fear and fascination. With my hands still gripping the steering wheel, I watched my boss examine his injuries in the rearview mirror. Blood and snot dripped from the man's nose and through his fingers.

"I'm bleeding," he said helplessly. "What should I do?" I imagined having to take him to New Rochelle Hospital, then having to hang out with him for a few hours. "Milt, I'm sorry. I didn't do it on purpose," I stammered stupidly.

"I need something...anything...a shirt, a clean rag. I have to stop the bleeding."

Milt found a pack of tissues in the glove compartment. He took a bunch and pressed them against his gushing forehead. For a brief moment, with a wad of bloody tissues on his forehead, he looked like Don Rickles playing a Jewish kamikaze pilot. When the tissues fell off, he growled. "Get outta the way. I'm driving."

Milt pushed me against the door as if I were a bulky package on the seat, giving me no choice but to get out of the car.

"Does this mean I'm fired? "

"No, it means you're a talented individual and I'm giving you a raise...Of course, it means you're fired!"

A few weeks later, I moved up in the world. Got myself hired to drive a taxicab.

Red Rover Taxi

All cab companies have their livery colors. Red Rover's were red and white. By the time Red Rover hired me in June of 1969, I was not breaking any new ground at the first black-owned cab company in New Rochelle. Two other young, white dudes already worked there. I was given the graveyard shift. My parents were deeply troubled.

The cab I was assigned belonged to a Jamaican man with one arm amputated at the biceps and a perpetual stogy hanging from his rictus. His name was Ingram Randolph and he was a far cry from the stereotypical dreadlocked, spliff-smoking, sun-splashed, happy Jamaican. His temper was as short as his hair. And he was bald, his head rippling with muscles. Randolph was an equal opportunity misanthropist. He hated everybody. And his anger was pyrotechnic, spellbinding—like the rumors that surrounded the loss of his arm. There were two: one, that it got blown off in Korea; the other, that he was in a bar fight in Kingston with a guy swinging a machete. The machete-man lost.

Stories are stories, but I saw that anger for myself one day when Randolph was standing around chatting with some of the fellas near the Coke machine. Out the window, he spotted a white cop ticketing his double-parked cab. He lit outside to talk his way out of the ticket. When that didn't work, he tore up the ticket with his teeth and spat it out in front of the cop and stormed back inside, where, without looking at anyone, he began hammering the side of the Coke machine with his tomahawk fist. "That offay, peckahwood, crackah sonofabitch! I shove de ticket right up his ass, mon."

He left fearful dents in the coke machine and an indelible message in my mind: *Go gently with his cab.*

~

And how about sex at the office? Her face was beautiful in its fine Nubian symmetry...Her ears were perfect shells...Her smile was a blazing, vanquishing whiteness. And she even had Kleenex in her purse...Look, Mr. Randolph, no jiz!!

~

It was midnight. Under a cloud-obscured sky, I found myself barreling down I-95 with two pimped-out, young gangstas in the back. The kind of cats Curtis Mayfield would rhapsodize in "Super Fly." Soon into the ride, after a prelude of spectacular lightning, it began to rain—not in pleasant droplets, but in racing sheets of water.

Because I didn't know how to work the defroster, the windows became blitzed in a milky white fog. With my palm, I kept rubbing little circles of clear viewing onto my windshield to see through. But from the back, I knew it must feel like we were driving in a four-sided box with a peephole.

The speed of the other cars, the chaos, the number of lanes—it was all new to me. From my boyhood, I'd already understood the wisdom of "never let 'em see you sweat," so I struggled not to let my panic—mounting by the minute—show. But you don't have to drive a taxi for long before you learn to pick up the mood of your passengers, and vice versa. Psychic bridges are built out of suppressed emotions. At a puddle on the highway, my car fishtailed slightly. With this first tiny loss of control, the young macks sensed my lack of confidence.

Soon they began a litany of advice and insults. It started with: "Turn on your lights, fool…" This was a legitimate request. I had been driving in complete darkness, swerving and fishtailing through the lanes without my headlights! When the lights flashed on, and we could suddenly see, I tried to play it off with a shrug.

"Everyone's got their own particular style. Know what I mean."

"Muthafucka, shut up and watch that truck!"

I had us caught in the back draft of a huge Allied Moving Van that was peeing buckets of filthy water on us from its mud-flaps.

"Hey man, get away from that truck!" boomed a second voice behind my ear.

"I'm trying…"

"What's wrong with yo' ass? Close that muthafuckin' window! Rain's comin' in."

"I can't," I lied. "The defroster's not working. If the window's not open, I can't see." I finger-scooped water from my left ear and wiped another little circle of clear patch with my hand.

"You trickin' for a dickin', or what? And what the fuck is up with that afro? Why you drivin' for a black company? You ain't black."

I did not answer. My attention was at full tilt just keeping us from veering into a truck in the next lane. The rain increased from a wild pelting to a wilder pelting. Rushing toward us was a fork in the road. The cab needed to stay to the right toward Bruckner Boulevard, but the force of the speeding moving van kept sucking us to the left, forcing us towards the Throgs Neck Bridge and Kennedy Airport.

A lot of cemeteries out that way, I reflected.

"Get away from that muthafuckin' truck, *NOW!*" one of the pimps screamed. "Slow this bitch down." He was leaning half his body into the front seat, spitting words in my ear. The truck's horn blasted him back into his seat.

I slowed down, trying to work myself free of the truck's gravitational pull. A car flying out my blind spot missed us by inches. My heart was in my throat. I didn't know which way I was going to die—in a heap of crumpled steel with a dozen other vehicles or with my throat slit from behind by my passengers. I flipped the cab to the right at the last possible moment and slipped around the truck, barely clearing its rear axle.

Once we were out of danger, the pimps began to roll on the backseat, laughing their asses off. "This must be the dumbest, unluckiest muthafucka in the world. And he's driving us to a card game. I think we already used up all our luck."

I tried to pretend I was invisible. Sticks and stones…

"The dumbest muthafucka!"

Gradually, the rain stopped. Once off the freeway, my passengers guided me down White Plains Road to a deserted street sparkling with broken glass, where rows of cars were double- and even triple-parked. The ones parked at the curb were going to stay awhile, whether they liked it or not.

The nightclub was on a corner in the middle of nowhere. Most of the golf-ball-sized lights on the flashing sign were broken. Out front, about twenty hard-looking dudes were standing around smoking and talking in clusters.

"Stop here." My passengers got out and didn't bother to close the doors or pay. I stuck my head out the window, and said, "What about my money?!"

"I got your money inside," one of the pimps laughed without

turning around. "You wanna come in and get it? I got your tip there too."

"Yeah, the tip of my dick," The other broad-brimmed brother quipped.

Even though I was leaving without the fare, I pulled away from the curb feeling happy to be alive. After the ride I had given them, I figured I was getting away lucky. I'd just have to eat the loss.

Nosing my way back through that dark maze of streets nullified by poverty, I ran a few lights as an invitation to a police escort that never came. Once back on I-95 and the relative safety of the Bartow Ave sign, it occurred to me that when all was said and done, I had just spent a harrowing hour and a half for diddley-squat, nothing, zilch. No, worse than that! I would have to go into my own pocket to cover the sixty percent that was the company's share—Randolph's money.[4]

Back at home base, I walked into the office and went directly to Frank Jefferson, the night dispatcher, to report the fiasco.

Frank was a man who had seen it all—the drama, the heartbreak and the glory of life. He was an ex-school teacher, forced into early retirement because of degenerative glaucoma. The headaches had gotten so bad he had to have his eyes surgically removed. Now he was completely blind. Around Red Rover everyone honored him as an accomplished jazz musician. Rumor had it he even recorded a session with Miles in the mid-Fifties.

Life had not been kind to Frank. Only two months after his son, a casualty of the Tet Offensive, came home in a body bag, Frank had lost his wife to breast cancer—on the same day Martin Luther King, Jr. was shot. With the blindness on top of that, it was more than anybody should have to bear.

---

[4] In 1969, suburban cabs in New Rochelle worked on a 60/40 split. The company got the larger share and paid for the gas.

I had taken in all these odd bits of information over the months I had been working there. As I parked opposite the office at North Avenue and Lincoln, I decided to level with Frank and tell him exactly what had happened. Maybe he'd lend me some money to cover my costs with Randolph.

With his shades on, sitting at his desk dispatching cabs on hot summer night, sipping Colt 45 from a paper bag, Frank seemed like a Homeric seer of kryptonite vision. With his jazz station playing softly in the background, he epitomized the spirit of bebop cool.

At first, being blind and probingly insightful, Frank had intimidated me. But one night, that all changed. We got into an argument about Jimi Hendrix. Frank said Hendrix didn't speak to the black community the way Smokey Robinson or the Temptations did. Therefore, he was not an authentic black artist. I disagreed.

From this back-and-forth, generation gap wrangling, we developed a crusty rapport. I didn't always agree with Frank, but he was fair and honest, and he taught me a lot. So, as I entered the office that night at around one A.M., these were the qualities I sought out.

The place was deserted, which was a relief. I pulled up a chair next to Frank, and began pouring out my soul, telling him how my passengers had abused me and walked away like princes in their own kingdom without paying me a dime. (I didn't mention the white-knuckled ride that set them off.)

"It happens," Frank said, calmly. "It's part of driving a cab."

"It was humiliating! They completely disrespected me."

"You learned something valuable tonight. In the street, as in life…R-E-S-P-E-C-T has got to be earned."

"I don't think they ever had any intention of paying."

"How do you know? Did you ask them for the money up front?"

"Are you kidding? Those guys would have killed me."

"Maybe not. Next time, let them know you expect to get paid."

"Yeah, well..." I wanted to ask him to front me some bread for Randolph but I couldn't do it.

"Don't sweat it. There's always tomorrow. By the way, your mother called. She wants you to call her."

"She called here? That's embarrassing..."

"Hey, a mother's son works the night shift, she's gonna worry. You ought be thankful. She loves you. I'd give anything to speak to my momma again, just one more time."

But I wasn't listening. What had happened stayed with me like bumps on a bad road. "Those guys walked right out on me," I said shaking my head. "No respect at all."

"Shake it off, man. This business is like that. Sometimes you're up. Sometimes you're down. Sometimes you're in the South Bronx and Bed-Sty. And sometimes you're up with the mansions and the big lawns. Forget it. Focus on what's right in front of you. The rest will take care of itself. My mother taught me that, and it's true."

His warm encouragement brought tears to my eyes, tears I tried to choke back. Was I really so stupid? Did I really know so little about life?

Frank put a hand on my shoulder, forearms heavily veined, silver bracelets jangling. "Hey, man, life is not for the weak-at-heart. You've gotta be strong. And that means, first and foremost, winning over your own defeatist attitude. Your mind, man..." Frank took a sip of malt liquor, and laid the brown bag gently on the desk. "Your mind is the greatest tool you have. It can be your worst enemy or your best friend. If you use it correctly, the way God intended, the possibilities are limitless."

As he spoke, the overhead fluorescent danced in his shades. I watched him hoist his sax and run nicotine-stained fingers up and down the neck. "Dream big, Marshall...And when you fail, fail big, that's the only way you'll ever do anything great."

He adjusted his mouthpiece and blew mad megahertz along with the radio. I sat there berating myself. I didn't know it, but I was undergoing the earliest stages of that strange mitosis—the psychic division and breaking apart that leads to becoming an artist. I had no talents, no direction, no abilities I could identify. And I hated myself for it. So how could I dare entertain Frank's theory of unlimited possibilities? Or plot out on the radar screen of my imagination—the blip-blip-blip payload of a Dream?

A Few Sufficiently Interesting Dispatchers & Fairway Louie

Q. How's business?
A. Picking up.

—A JOKE TOLD REPEATEDLY BY FAIRWAY LOUIE

Good dispatchers are, for the most part, quick-witted, succinct, get-to-the-point kind of guys, with a habitually sarcastic edge. The best are highly capable chess masters, visualizing several moves at once. They track you. They set you up. They feed you. They know how the game is played and expect the same of you. When they slam dunk your pockets, it only stands to reason they want a little something in return. This is the language of money, spoken in the currency of finesse. Whether they use a double negative or double entendre, their fluid patter sets a tone. You look forward to their presence on the radio.

When most people in the general public think *cab dispatcher,* they conjure up Danny DeVito's character on the TV show "Taxi." A big fish in a small pond. A nasty little twerp who likes to throw his weight around. Sequestered in the safety of his cage, he stands above the fray, fighting the street wars from a command post out of harm's way. Well, Louie, for all his morally corrupt ways, was a boy scout compared to a guy I worked for in New Rochelle in the early '70s.

Chicky would not only leave the cage, if you gave him any lip—he'd hijack one of his own cabs and track you down. Then he would pull you out of the cab by a fistful of shirt and threaten to kick your ass if you didn't shape up. Mussolini and Fabian—genetically engineer a hybrid of these two men, and then subtract 30 points from the hybrid's IQ, and you'd end up with Chicky. Sporting roach killers so pointy they could inflict stab wounds.

Chicky was the manager, chief dispatcher and *Capo* for New Mall Taxi, which had an office located in the New Rochelle train station. He wore his hair in a slick pompadour, and always had a comb sticking out his back pocket. The look was out of style by at least a decade, but this didn't faze Chicky. Any reflecting surface he could find—a window, a mirror, a bald head—he'd be mugging in it, admiring his pockmarked face and combing his hair, of which every last strand was precisely set in goo.

He was a man of forty, bossing around a bunch of kids barely out of high school, or in their early twenties, who thought he was a clown. Once, in a megalomaniacal fit of anger, he fired the whole fleet. There were about ten cabs parked on the upper level on the other side of the train tracks. About eight of us drivers were crowded into someone's cab passing a joint. Chicky's voice came squelching over the radio.

"Every last one of yuz, listen up." Chicky was a master of the pregnant pause. "Take the wax out ladies…YUZ ALL FIRED!" Then, ten minutes later, when the train came in and he was mobbed by hordes of angry customers demanding cabs, he reinstated all of us with a threat. "I feel sorry for anyone dumb enough not to be down here in three minutes. Did I say three minutes? Excuse me, I meant two minutes…Fifty-seven seconds, fifty-six…."

He once saw me reading "The Selected Poems of Ezra Pound" and plucked the book out of my hands, saying, "Hmmm…*Ezriah* Pound. A nice Jewish boy. You Jews stick together, don't you?"

"Chicky, Ezra Pound was an anti-Semite."

"So am I..." Chicky said, and got me in a headlock.

Human hierarchies seem to be inescapable. Someone is always on the top slinging shit, and someone is always on the bottom, catching it. In the cab world, there is always one driver in particular whom the dispatcher singles out for repeated abuse. In almost every case, the guy brings it on himself. After a driver failed several times to copy an address correctly, I once heard a dispatcher tell him over the air, "Next time, write the numbers in reverse on your forehead and look in the mirror. And by the way, have you ever considered suicide?"

In this game of pitch-and-catch, my fantasy battery would pair "Chicky, the dispatcher" with a driver named Fairway Louie. Fairway Louie was an escapee from an insane asylum known as Grasslands, where he boasted of having received 70 shock treatments and 10 ice baths. He was also an ex-caddy, whose reputation got him blackballed from every golf course in Lower Westchester County. He worked with me at Blue Jay Taxi in New Rochelle. And, through feats of incredible ineptitude, he turned himself into a legend. "Fairway Lou-botomy" they used to call him. I once saw him back up into mailbox so hard he knocked it off its mounting, then drive away with a dented bumper[5] and a smashed rear taillight, as if nothing had happened. But by far his greatest performance—and the thing that got him fired—was the Theresa Higgins incident.

Theresa Higgins was a Broadway actress who called a Blue Jay Taxi to take her from her palatial home in Scarsdale to her performance at a theater in Midtown. How she wound up in Brooklyn, weeping her eyes out in the back seat of Fairway Louie's cab, is something only Louie himself could answer. "I'm

[5] Please remember that in those days a bumper was a formidable object.

ruined. I missed my show..." That's how Hecky McCann, the dispatcher, re-telling the story to a bunch of us, mimicked her grief in falsetto. "I'll never work again...And neither will you, mister."

As if on cue, a cockroach crawled across his desk. Hecky watched it over his big beer gut, and pointed as the insect crossed beyond a plateau of papers. "Here's another sonofabitch who's not gonna make it."

After he slammed it into extinction, Hecky McCann wiped his hand on his pants, and said to one of his lieutenants, a 300-lb. speed freak with greasy skin and greasy hair called *Nemo, the Whale,* "Is that lunch wagon still out there?"

"I don't know."

"Well, take a look, you fat sonofabitch." Nemo stood up with a groan and looked out the window. "Is he still there?"

"Yeah, he's still there."

"Good. Get me a hot dog with everything on it."

The Ride

The patron saint of taxi drivers is St. Fiacre, named after the Hotel St. Fiacre in Paris, where horse-drawn cabs were first observed in the late 19th century.

—DESK REFERENCE, NEW YORK PUBLIC LIBRARY

San Francisco was still buzzing on Sunday night, September 24, 1995, in the wake of the Folsom Street Fair, a wild, leather manifest and Mephistoed, gay-prom pilgrimage of a party, which every year brings in tens of thousands of tourists from all over the world. With so many drunken revelers in the street, you couldn't go more than a few car lengths without somebody diving out, screaming, "TAXI!"

My first fare, against all odds, was a family of camera-wielding, suburban spies from Walnut Creek, all in a huff about "the nudity" and "disgusting behavior."

"Well, isn't that the whole point?" I said to Dad.
"This is a sex carnival, the Great America of whips 'n' chains and bondage. Not something you take teenagers to..." *Moron!*

I dropped them at the Embarcadero BART. And to my amazement, in spite of the lecture, he gave me a tip.

Four drunken sailors stationed at the Treasure Island Naval Base got in. "Take us to see the FREAKS," their leader shouted. I studied him, as he lifted his baseball cap to smooth his matted hair. The tight headband left a line of red dots encoded in his forehead, which I translated to mean, *I have shit for brains.* "Traffic is slammed," I said. "I'll get you as close as I can."

South-of-Market, the exodus was in high gear. My passengers, engulfed in this proud spectacle of queerness, began yelling insults. An old boy in leather chaps, whose sagging butt looked like the draped curtain at the Castro Theatre, waved and gave us a creepy smile. In big letters, his tee-shirt read *SUBMIT!*

"Keep your grandpa in the house and buy him some fucking pants, will ya?" my passenger clowned with his buddy.

Focused on the complete standstill a block ahead, I was cursing up a storm, when these guys got into it with a woman walking by with a python draped around her brightly tattooed shoulders. Thankfully, after an initial trade-off, she took the high road and ignored their obscene gestures. Not so with the midget in red spandex pants, who stopped what he was doing to promptly flip us off with both hands, gunslinger-style. Satisfied his mojo had done the job, he went back to leading a king-sized queen on a leash and hissing at the sailors: "Oh, Mona, get a life!"

Me? I was at the end of my rope. Idiots, traffic, tension—I busted a move.

"Hang a U-terus! I like the way this guy drives," one of the sailors said. I had them bouncing off each other in the back, like malicious molecules.

"End of the line fellas...You owe me $6.40." I said, slamming the brakes.

A collection ensued. Everyone began digging and fumbling through their pockets, complaining about who paid last and how much. I can't tell you what kind of slow torture this is for a cab driver—watching one crumpled bill after another get counted out and placed on the console, while all around you people are hovering, desperate to get in.

A German tourist with a camcorder was tapping on my window, asking directions to the Golden Gate Bridge. I ignored him.

A guy with a fifth of Gilbey's gin approached the door on the passenger's side. Pah-pop!! went the automatic locks. He slapped the window and screamed over to his friends, "I got a cab! I got a cab!"

No you don't, shitface! That's why I picked *him* up—the guy waving to me near the Burger King at 8th & Market. He was waving and jogging toward me with dry cleaning slung over his shoulder. I watched his lanky strides. Old school Fila gear under a leather jacket. I could identify with a guy like this, a working stiff, trying to get home.

"Man, am I glad to see you! Thanks for picking me up."

"No problem," I said, pulling down the visor against the metallic glare of the dying sun. He was sitting diagonal to me on the right side, the way I prefer. The clean shirts were on his lap—in a slightly torn, plastic garment bag with a clothier's emblem that zippered up the front.

"Where would you like to go?" I asked.

"HP…Hunters Point…"

I thought about it.

Did I really want to pull myself off this paper-chase and wind up in a dangerous neighborhood—and maybe even risk my life? For what? To fulfill my part in the social contract? Corporations aren't doing it. The rich and powerful certainly aren't sending that message. They sneer at the very mention of social responsibility. Yet cab drivers, often viewed as second-class citizens, are required by law to risk their lives. Well, well…

Fact: a racial cold war exists in America.

Fact: no one confronts these tensions more personally than a cab driver.

Fact: he/she has the opportunity to implement social change more directly and sincerely than any politician on the stump.

"Where, specifically, in Hunters Point are you going?" I asked.

"Kiska Road, off Ingalls, I'll show you…" We inched past a throng of weary faces waiting for the bus.

"Give up on the bus?" I asked.

"Muni? On a night like this? You gotta be kidding!" he snickered. I hit the brakes. His head flew back and bumped against the window.

"You okay, man?"

"Yeah. But peep that!"

A gorgeous young woman, clad only in Saran wrap and glittery pumps, walked out defiantly in front of my slow-moving cab. The feline grace of her swaying hips held us speechless for a second. Behind her, traipsing martyr-like, was a guy covered in Christmas decorations hung with paper clips all over his naked body. He was bleeding in a polka-dot pattern of drying scabs.

"Why would anybody do that to himself?" I asked.

"Man, I don't know. It's a buncha crazy San Fran-sissy-co shit to me."

I checked him out in the mirror. He was about my age, tall and lean with a grizzled goatee. "Sounds like you're not from around here."

"Originally from De-troit."

"This sun is murder!" I said, adjusting my visor.

"For real," he said. A hand speckled with bits of cement or mud shielded his eyes against the sun.

"I'm finna fall asleep right here…been workin' since four in the morning." He yawned and slouched down low in the seat. Someone falling asleep on you—that's not cool. At some point, you have to wake them up. And sometimes, when blasting the radio and salvos of bitter curses aren't enough, you have to start shaking them, and that *really* ain't cool.

"Please don't fall asleep..."

He looked at me with tired lids. I was eating licorice, making sucking noises, trying to get a nasty little piece unstuck from my back molars. "Want some licorice?" I reached across the seat and rattled the box.

"No, thank you."

"Kiska Road is up on the hill, isn't it?"

"Yeah. Take Army to Bayshore...I'll show you from there."

Unexpectedly, someone pounded his fist on the back of the cab. I jumped. "It's a zoo out here," I said, weaving around a stalled vehicle, and getting off Market to Valencia.

Hunter's Point...was a dangerous place. I'd been up there twice in the past few weeks. Once, to drop off an old lady and her deaf grandson whom I'd picked up at Kaiser Hospital; and once to take a massage parlor nymph to her doorstep in the Double Rock projects, in the wee hours of the morning. She told me she was starting her own out-call service, webpage, nine-hundred number and all. She was all excited about the future, singing her dreams in the key of ME, ME, ME!

I thought about my own dreams and felt the gnawing in my gut of vast and unfulfilled ambitions. A life (without credentials) devoted to art—the M.A. and the Ph.D. that legitimize even a poet's career in this society. I was out of the loop, wasting my life driving a cab.

Only a few days ago, traveling back down those serpentine streets of Hunter's Point, I'd made eye contact with a kid "grinding" on the corner, selling drugs under a pus-colored, twitching streetlight. He vibed me with a hate-filled, ghetto stare, and went into his jacket like he was reaching for a gun. The pantomime had enraged me...

"I ain't goin'!" I told the guy with the dry cleaned shirts. "Too dangerous."

He sat up in the seat. "Excuse me?"

"I'm not going up to Kiska Road." I repeated in a calmer voice. "It's too dangerous..."

I half expected him to say, "All right, what's your badge number? I'm reporting you to the Taxi Detail." But he said, "Why you say it's too dangerous...Black folks live up there. They gotta get home too!"

"Yeah, I know..." At the light, I turned around and said, "I'll be honest with you, man. I don't feel comfortable going up there." He looked unconvinced.

"Why don't you try another cab?" It was a classic example of having said yes to something before I had thought it through.

"I don't want another cab. I want *this* cab!" He ended with a loud exhalation that was a message from a long bloodline of rejection and disgust.

Here we go again. "You wanna go somewhere else? I'll take you somewhere else," I said, aware of how ridiculous this was.

"*My friend,* I wanna go home. I'm dead on my feet. That's why I'm springin' for a cab, not ridin' the bus. Please..."

"*My friend,* I had a bad experience up there..."

"What kind of bad experience?" he said, sounding genuinely interested.

"Look, I jus' ain't goin' up on that hill, period. So what do you wanna do. Go somewhere else—or catch another cab?"

"It'll take forever to get another cab. You know that."

I did know that, but I wasn't budging.

"Okay, brother-man, since you don't like *hills...*" The sarcasm was loud and clear. "Take me to the Balboa BART...I'll go to my sister's place and catch a ride from there. Is that cool?"

"Sure. How do you wanna go?"

"You the driver. Go any way you like. But make it fast," he said, slouching back down in his seat.

We flew down Valencia, past the cop-shop, the chic shops, the restaurants, the nite spots and the coffee hangouts, all teched-out and gentrified. I wanted to ask him where he worked and what he did for a living. But I didn't want to bother him any more. "Wanna hear some music? Or you wanna snooze?" I asked in a friendly voice.

"Snooze is better...It's been a long day."

On the freeway, I snapped on my seatbelt and let him sleep. All four lanes were moving. The incinerated shell of a car that had caught fire and brought the entire freeway to a halt the night before was still parked on the shoulder of the road.

I took 101 to 280 and thought about this rapper I'd picked up last night or the night before—driving a cab the nights bleed into one another so it's hard to keep track. He was a big cat with gold fronts and dreads, flashing money, high-visible at the corner of Eddy & Taylor, going to the East Bay, the Oakland ghetto where the benches at bus stops rhapsodize Rap CDs and the billboards depicting running shoes emit electro-magnetic force fields that give the ghetto youth the kiss of corporate collusion.

I picked this kid up and he absolutely blew my mind—rhyming over the radio off the top of his dome—flippin' mad crazy shit about the erector-set girders of the Bay Bridge, the interior of my cab, the fact that the vertical line was missing from the dollar sign on my meter, so that it read "sextras." And he did it with such amazing virtuosity, I gave him my phone number and said, "Here, you gotta teach me how to do that!"

As I thought about that ride—the unexpected beauty of it—

I decided to shave a couple of bucks off the meter for my drowsy *friend.*

About a quarter of a mile from the Ocean-Geneva turn-off, the exit sign loomed into view. I moved into the right lane, preparing to get off. Suddenly, with the swiftness of a striking snake, the man in the backseat had a garrote over my head, and a box-cutter knife on my neck. Through clenched teeth, he hollered: "Drive muthafucka, or I'll kill you!"

With a knife on my neck and my heart racing at top speed, time stood still. I couldn't believe it. I was screwed, glued and tattooed!! And me—a veteran of the streets for how many years?

In an Ice Age lasting nanoseconds, I saw myself in split-screen craning down from above in an out-of-body panorama. And yet here I was, a man behind the wheel of his taxi, reconstructing the whole emotional history of human betrayal. *Judas, nodding deceitfully in the torchlight of Gethsemane. Caesar, dying in the river of his own blood, shocked beyond belief by what he sees in his friend's eyes, wondering how could this be happening?* And to make matters worse, my own seatbelt (which I never use except on the freeway) was trapping me! What fucked-up irony!

Shirts on hangers—what a lovely ploy! This guy got in planning mischief. From the very beginning, he planned to do this to me—strangling device under his shirts.

In a state of mounting confusion, I went limp. My brain—with its ten billion neurons, each equipped with two hundred firing synapses—went down in a fizzle of imploding light. In numbed amazement, I sat there watching the deep purple sky with its appalling beauty. I knew what it was to be an animal caught in a trap. I knew what it was to be a man thinking his last thoughts. I also knew I had to do something, or I was going to die.

With a flick of the wheel, I sent us careening from the off-ramp, back onto the freeway. It was Sunday, with Sunday evening traffic, 8:06, and we were lucky no one was behind us or we'd have been toast—demolition derby style. Next thing I know, I'm steering with my knees, going for the garrote.

In the counter-attack, the reversal, the confusion—he relaxed his grip. And with my left hand, I snatched at the garrote—chin down and in to protect my neck and avoid a fatal slice. With my right hand, I tried to knock the box cutter free with a quick, sharp, upturned palm. But instead of hitting his hand, I hit the razor-blade. It cut me. There was blood. The cab lurched forward. I got off the gas, and steadied the wheel with my left hand, watching in a trance as we drifted along in slow motion between lanes. Then I hit the brake, and slammed it into park and killed the engine. And just as sudden as that, recognizing how vulnerable we had both become, he stopped his attack.

It was so insane, sitting there in my cab taking stock of myself. A streak of blood on the wheel, some blood on my pants. Otherwise, everything was normal. Just hunky-dory. The meter, ticking away, said I was hired. The dispatcher was calling out orders, lecturing someone on the finer points of radio etiquette. The numbers three-zero-seven were reversed in yellow tape on the windshield, as were the red digits from the meter. The Motorola radio was within reach, only a grab away. But then the brutal reality of the situation reasserted itself. What could I do? I was in the Twilight Zone, marooned on the periphery of a dream, sticking out at an angle between lanes two and three, mocking the most impossible scenarios for help.

Leaning on their horns, cars and trucks ripped past us, angrily. Hi-beams blazed in a lunatic onslaught. After the bright bursts came the dark shadows—and a stillness that could almost be called meditative. We sat there in the crosshairs, playing a game of "ultimate poker"...*See you my life, raise you your own...* A tour bus and a shiny gas truck with a flame-emblem birthmarked to its flank descended upon us in tandem. The back draft shook my Dodge Stratus wildly from side to side.

We were going to get rear-ended. It was only a matter of time. Caught in the riptide of this fearful realization, he had retreated to the back of the cab! Capitalizing on this, I unbuckled my seat-belt and spun around. I took the offensive and began shouting like a madman, "Get the fuck outta my cab! Get the fuck out, NOW, BITCH!!"

He didn't respond. He didn't do anything or even seem to hear me. He was curled up in the back seat peering out the window, looking for the phantom fireball emanating from his cracked-out mind, the fatal blow that would consume him. Meanwhile, in the immortal words of Sun Tzu, author of "The Art of War," I was "using the terrain"—using the minefield of the freeway to fight back.

We had both made mistakes. Mine was in judgment. His was in timing. Had he held off his attack another two seconds, I would have been dead meat—a quarry to be toyed with, begging for my life in the swaying trees and vast hush of McClaren Park, only blocks away. But he'd blown it by not waiting until we were off the freeway.

There was blood on my shirt and my new denim jacket. My fingers were sticky with blood. And as I kept discovering blood, blood, blood—I got it in my head that he had cut my neck too! And this set off my own mounting panic. It was a sure thing, given our coordinates, that in a short time, we'd go the way of most freeway wrecks—launched, flipped and multiple gang-banged by oncoming traffic in a cold orgy of Death.

But then he said something that changed everything. He said, "Please drive the car, muthafucka! You're gonna kill us both!"

I looked at him. His eyes were bulging out of his head like demented ping-pong balls. *Please drive the car muthafucka. You're gonna kill us both?* This guy was full of surprises. And that—was a brilliant line. What would he say next, "Hey, I'm only joking. Drive over to the side and let's pretend this never happened?"

"No, shithead, you're gonna fuckin' die!" I yelled in his crack-head face. He was focused out the window, hanging from the heels of his smoked-out mind, watching the charge of the light brigade. Scrunched up in the corner, he held the box cutter up to his ear, as if he were listening to it—like a cell phone or a transistor radio or a conch shell—shrinking physically, going fetal—losing it all to the poison of fear.

For a fleeting moment, I wanted to kill him. If I'd had a gun, I think I would have. But then I saw myself mirrored in his face—a sweating face, an ancient mask from the Niger Valley, floating through hysterical sequences of shadow and glare, darkness and blinding light. Like me, he was a man looking for a way out.

I fired up the ignition. It was an automatic, stick on the floor. He spun around and looked at me with a new, heightened insanity. I yelled some wild crazy shit in his face. "Abracadabra, I'm gonna reach out and grab ya..." or something equally ludicrous. He mugged stupefied, not knowing what to do. I did—scanning the mirror in three rapid shots of adrenaline eyes, going point-to-point, counting down, pumping up, activating, modulating, irradiating every cell in my body.

I looked, I prayed, I estimated, I popped it into neutral and released the hand-brake—and rolling along at 5 mph, I bailed. Next thing, I'm standing in the middle of the freeway—door hanging open—looking at the predator, savoring the terror in his eyes, enjoying my brief moment of revenge, as he realized he was rolling down 280 with no driver!

Caught flat-footed on the four-lane highway, a black Forerunner was bearing down on me like a demon with halogen eyes. As he swept past, I felt the thunder of two hundred and fifty stampeding horses giddy-up right through me.

Then I jogged off the tarmac and made it to safety, elated beyond belief that, twice within a matter of minutes, I had escaped Death.

Standing behind the guardrail, I watched the man who'd tried to kill me scramble madly into the front seat, grab the wheel, and drive off in a karmic carjack that killed no one—not him, or me, or some innocent family, traveling home under crossed stars on the shit-happens highway.

And no, they never caught him.

The investigation was a spiritless, half-hearted affair. They called it a robbery, since the cab was stolen. I guess almost getting your throat cut doesn't count for much, if you foil the attempt. They found the cab, deserted in Visitacion Valley on the outskirts of McClaren Park. But the oddest and, by far, the most bizarre part of this investigation was that, according to the police the guy didn't leave any prints. The cab was full of prints, but they belonged to me and to the Arab driver who had the shift before me. But there was nothing of his—not a single swirl pattern for the lab boys to I.D.

2

KISS MY REAR AXLE

SFPD/AUTHORITY—1077(a) M.P.C.

III. Definitions

"Medallion Holder" as used in these Taxicab Regulations means any permittee licensed by the City and County of San Francisco to own and operate a taxicab.

"Taxicab Driver" as used in these Taxicab Regulations means any permittee licensed by the Chief of Police of the City and County of San Francisco to drive a taxicab.

"Research conducted three year ago at London's Institute of Neurology found that the brains of cabbies actually grow to a larger-than-average size after years on the job," reports the BBC News Online. Specifically, the hippocampus enlarges and adapts to help them store a detailed mental map of the city...Next time you have just minutes to get to the airport and you put your fate in the hands of a taxi driver, take comfort in this: Chances are, that taxi driver has a bigger brain than you do."[6]

---

[6] Chase, Nicholas, "Why Taxi Drivers Have Bigger Brains"

Sometimes the Nicest People Can Kill You

In San Francisco, a new driver (unless he knows someone) gets the shittiest cabs to drive and works the day shift. When I started driving at Desoto in the fall of 1981, Saturday thru Wednesday were my assigned days. I hated it. Working *days* didn't suit me. I liked to go out and party, which meant I would stumble in at noon and barely make my gates[7] and gas. This made me feel like an indentured servant. And though it was nobody's fault but my own, it made me very depressed hanging around a cab yard with a hangover, waiting for hours at a time to go to work! Like many other drivers, I had assigned days but no assigned cab, which meant I had to wait for someone to come in off the street and short shift.[8]

On the day of the incident, I arrived at the Desoto garage at 7 A.M. hoping to get out quickly. At 11:30 A.M. my cab finally arrived. I was in the bathroom peeing, straddling a puddle on the floor. On the wall, above an ancient urinal streaked with rust, some malcontent had written,

ARTIST=BUM

---

[7] Gates=rental for cab.

[8] A "short-shift" makes it possible for a driver to cash out midway through his eleven-hour shift and go home. He pays a pro-rated fee. The driver taking his place pays full gates (i.e., the full cost of the shift) and the company makes bank twice.

I glanced in the broken mirror and saw a thirty year old guy with salt 'n' pepper hair and bags under his eyes, wearing a black leather jacket. The urinal was still flushing loudly as the wooden door banged shut behind me. A tired-looking man with a middle-age paunch peeled himself out of the cab, complaining of a backache.

"Take your sweet time, bro, but I've been waiting since seven this morning. I wanna get outta here."

"That's your problem..." the driver growled. He slowly pulled his waybill[9] out from the visor, wrote down his mileage and handed it to the gasman, who recorded the numbers in a ledger.

We locked eyes. I slapped my clipboard against my thigh. "Silver..." I heard my name.

"Silver..." The cashier summoned me through a raspy microphone. I went back into the driver's room and stood before a window of four-inch bulletproof glass.

"Medallion's in the cab," the cashier said. She slid my waybill out a little chute. I put my tip in the same hole. "Have this cab back no later than five. Five o'clock sharp, okay? A minute over and you got problems."

I turned and said nothing. Found the cab empty and climbed in. Driving a filthy piece-of-shit is very demoralizing, and this cab was filthy, inside and out. A fine patina of filth glazed the windshield. The odometer showed 283,000-plus miles. How the guy drove it in this condition I don't know. I went over to the water hose and gave it a quick shower. Blasts of water sent black dirt dripping off the blue cab with white trim. On the front door passenger's side where some ornamental siding had torn off, greasy black fluid ran through the two peepholes that remained.

---

[9] "Waybill" aka trip sheet—where all rides are logged by time, destination and fee.

Nosing my way outta the garage, waiting for traffic, I could feel the tension mounting. I had just spent four long hours waiting for a short shift with a U.N. delegation of miserable-looking comrades, cooped up in the driver's room—which isn't really a room at all, but an enclosed area, set off from the lube rack, the parked cabs, and the air-hose, by an ancient row of green lockers, dented from punches and kicks, and furry along the top with what had to be decades of dust. I sat there reading *I, Claudius* under a cloud of smoke, with fifteen other drivers...one of them a chain-smoking, German woman with the hard-wiring of a woodpecker, who kept saying, "Fucking assholes, these fucking assholes...Who do these owners think they are? Fucking assholes!!"

I took a deep breath and exhaled slowly. I could see why the guy had complained about his back. The seat was broken—stuck at a weird angle. And the constant blasts of white noise from the radio that occurred between transmissions assaulted the mind like sonic hand grenades. But these were relatively minor annoyances compared to the great big glaring fact: The brakes sucked! At 15 mph, when I tapped them, the cab jerked sharply to the right. I drove down Post Street, trying to get a feel for the steering. The doorman at the St. Francis blew his whistle and made a wing-flapping gesture with his arms. *Airport.*

In the world of cab drivers, "airport" may be the sexiest word in the English language. To get to him, I played a dangerous game of chicken with a group of slow-moving pedestrians. I zoomed up in front of the hotel, jumped out and opened up my trunk.

The doorman said, "American Airlines," as he loaded in an overnight bag and a set of golf clubs. My passenger, a Terry Bradshaw look-alike, wearing an Aloha shirt, handed off a tip with the speed of a corner drug dealer and belched, "Yeah, buddy," in my face. The doorman pocketed the thrice-folded bill, and then looked at me with the expectation of more...

Yeah, right...

When I started up the cab, the guy slathered in toucans says, "Havin' a good day, *CHIEF?*"

Nothing like being called *CHIEF* by an aging, yuppie smartass.

So I said, "Excellent, *Chief.* How you doin', *Chief?*" I had him two chiefs to one. Maybe he'd get the message.

"I'm doin' great. Beautiful day!" he beamed.

"Whadya mean? It's about to rain."

"When you get my age, every day above ground is a beautiful day." Another sonic hand grenade fulminated from the cab radio. "Hey, can you turn that damn thing off."

"Absolutely. After a while you get so desensitized...You don't hear it."

"That noise would drive me crazy."

We were caught behind the clang-clang-clangor of a cable car. "Love your town. Great town, San Fran..."

"First time visiting?"

"Heck, no, but I love it. I always have a great time here."

In front of us, the cable car was having problems. The brakeman jumped out and waved his arms at me. "Cabbie, go around. Go around, man."

I blitz the illegal left on O'Farrell and head down Stockton.

"Hey, look at this!" my passenger screamed. "My lucky day! I just found a hundred dollar bill on your back seat!"

"Oh, really?"

"Yes, sir. I'm one lucky dog."

"I hope you know the virtues of sharing."

"Say what? Buddy, the only thing I share is pain."

"Well, I know you're enjoying this traffic jam then."

What a mess! The green light came and went three times.

Pedestrians jaywalked. The electric bus right in front of us lost power and jerked to a halt. Its antenna, dangling overhead, threw off a flourish of sparks.

"We missed the goddamn light again!" I yelled.

"You own this cab?"

"No, I'm just a driver. A humble driver."

"How much does a medallion cost in San Fran? They're like a hundred and fifty grand in New York."

"That's not how it works here." I went through the whole megillah. "The SFPD issues them. You put your name on a list, pay a fee and then, in ten, fifteen, twenty years, you're an owner. Technically, since 1979, there are no medallion owners in San Francisco. Only medallion holders. It's not your property. You can't transfer it to anyone else and it reverts to the city when you die. That's how the law reads, but sharpies figure a way around it."

"Did you put your name on the list? "

"Hell, no! If I'm driving a cab in fifteen or twenty years, I hope someone shoots me."

"If I were you I'd put my name on that list!"

"Fuck that! This is a temporary gig. I swear to you, if I'm driving a cab fifteen years from now, I'll kill myself."

The Muni driver still hadn't fixed the antenna. The cab behind me leaned on his horn. We peekabooed around the disabled bus and almost got clobbered by some dickhead running a red on Market. I yelled visceral obscenities.

"Sometimes the nicest people can kill you," my passenger said.

"That's beautiful. I'll make a note of that."

Suddenly, the world around us darkened to silent beauty and the wind started kicking up. Wild tentacles of electricity danced in the charcoal sky. Then came a boom and a crack and a few fat pellets of rain fell on the windshield.

"It's about to get stupid out here," I said.

"Baby, the rain must fall..."

By the time we reached the freeway, a few more pellets had fallen, but not enough to keep the wipers (one blade going clockwise, the other going counter-clockwise) from scraping on the windshield. Then, all hell broke loose. Rain came down in torrents—nails and javelins of water, followed by a furious bombardment of hailstones bouncing insanely all over the road. At the legendary hospital curve, traffic slowed to a halt.

"Feels like Miami...Goddamn! I had no idea it rained this hard out here!"

"Acid rain..." I grumbled.

"You don't know the first thing about acid rain!"

I told him I had just read a big article about acid rain in *Time* magazine.

He said, "Fuck *Time* magazine! Acid rain doesn't exist. It's a fraud, an ecological lie!" He was vehement, leaning forward and putting a headlock on the headrest. I felt the challenge in my gonads.

"Tell that to the guy in Ontario, Canada...his green Chevy van was speckled with blue droplets after the acid leached out the yellow. In my book, that's acid rain..."

"Left-wing, liberal hokum." In the force of the downpour, the broken dome light sprang a leak and water started dripping in on us.

"Can we stick something in here? I'm getting soaked..." I handed him my paperback—*I, Claudius*—the first thing available. "Great book," he said, leafing through the pages. "Ever hear the term 'Naumachia'?"

I told him, "No, but I know what pneumonia is. Stand in the acid rain too long and you'll get it..."

He gave a big, hearty laugh and handed back my book, saying he didn't want to ruin it. "Since you're reading *I, Claudius* you might be interested to know that the Romans used to stage mock-sea battles called Naumachia. Claudius staged the largest one ever on Lake Fucinus...19,000 combatants, 50 vessels in an all-out fight to the death...By the way, the name is Cliff."

"How do you know such arcane facts, Cliff?"

"I'm a military historian. Well, not any more. I'm retired now."

"Sean." We shook hands. "Two opposing navies in a fight to the death," I repeated.

"That's right. The greatest show on earth..." Cliff said.

As suddenly and violently as the rain had come, that's how quickly it stopped—leaving the freeway in a cold iridescence of silvery tones. Within minutes, the sun was peeking through and traffic picked back up to normal speed.

We were cruising. I started thinking about this Japanese girl I was seeing. Accidents happen when the mind drifts...

Up ahead, the sun broke through. A broad shaft of exceedingly fine-spun gold fell across the road. At 65 mph, I saw red taillights, flaring in front of me—the cars piling up in a slow, screeching, inevitable ballet of doom. In my panic, I slammed the brakes—a bad move that sent us hydroplaning into a wild skid. Fighting the skid, instead of going with it, I spun us 180° in the wrong direction, fishtailing this way and that, until we found ourselves in the path of a cement truck, coming at us full bore, like a massive rhino.

Cliff yelled something. I said, "Oh, fuck!" And we plunged leagues below the surface of the event, to where the mind perceives all in calm detachment. We collided obliquely—and it was nothing. A glancing shot, a ping—that sent us flying softly into the highway shrubbery.

When it was over, the cement driver and I got out and looked at each other with sheer amazement. Then we checked the damage and exchanged information. During all this, my passenger Cliff sat in the cab grimacing and massaging his neck, complaining of whiplash, which he probably wasn't faking. I called the dispatcher and told him to send an ambulance for Cliff and a tow-truck for me.

As they lifted Cliff onto the gurney, he called out for his luggage and golf clubs. The paramedic explained it was against company policy to take along personal belongings.

"Besides...It's the cab's responsibility to make sure your stuff is safe. They're criminally liable."

I told him, no worries. I'll take care of your stuff. He waved his hand and disappeared into the maw of the meat wagon.

Back at the barn, every eye followed the damaged cab being towed in. Shifts were changing and cabs were semi-circled in a queue, waiting to be gassed and have their oil checked. Bing, a tall, lanky, sixty-year-old black man in greasy blue coveralls, red rag hanging out his back pocket, walked out to meet the tow-driver and survey the damage. The driver handed him a clipboard to sign.

The tow rumbled up the ramp and dumped his cargo—not too bad, a smashed headlight and caved-in front bumper. I was expecting to be fired, but the manager had already gone for the day. "You're lucky," Bing said, puffing on his pipe. "I would have fired your ass."

"I'm lucky I wasn't hurt."

"If you were hurt and you filed for Workman's Comp, they'da fire your ass for sure! It's an unwritten law."

I walked back to the driver's room to meet with the accident investigator. She was using the pool table as a desk, her elbows resting on worn velvet.

From her attaché case, she pulled out a bunch of papers and said, “Here, fill in the diagrams and all the pertinent info, then write down everything that happened…”

“Everything? ”

“Everything.”

Ten feet away, suspended from the ceiling by two slender chains a long wooden sign read,

DEATH LURKS AT INTERSECTIONS

“Can I use you’re pen? Mine’s out of ink.” The accident investigator tossed me a pen. My hand was still trembling as I started to write.

Sex in a Taxi

"...let's see if you can bring bring bring
the nasty out of me..."
—MISSY ELLIOTT

Once upon a time, back when you could fuck a total stranger and not have to wear a condom, back in the summer of 1984, when I started driving a cab at night in San Francisco—the aura and possibility of spontaneous sex with a stranger saturated the air like poppers. Straight or gay, it was the hothouse environment we all lived in. In the cab with random women, it was the ghost in the dialogue, the high-voltage rail, humming beneath the words. Back then, when AIDS was called GRID, and only the science editor of the newspaper seemed to care, I met Angelica for the third time in my cab.

The first time we met was a disaster. We smoked some dope in the cab, and wound up in her apartment. She was down to her Victoria's Secret lingerie, and I was good to go, dry humping those voluptuous curves. But the chick was too drunk for sex. She kept falling off her bed and giving me this pie-eyed look of *I'm sorry. Oops...I did it again.* I don't have time for this horseshit! I said politely, and split. But San Francisco is a small town and, a year later, she hopped in my cab for a second time. After some early awkwardness, we started to click. The conversation rolled. She gave me the digits. I filed the number away.

A couple of months later, on the Friday night of Fleet Week, trying not to get bogged down in that endless morass of bicyclists known as Critical Mass, I made a quick drop-off at the Pickwick Hotel at 5th & Mission. Before I could slam the door shut, a young woman got in. It was Angelica!

"Three's a charm," I said.

She didn't get it. It took a moment for her to recognize me. Then, she let out a big *"Sean!!"* and gave me a hug. Now I was confused, until I remembered that Sean was my cab driving persona. As we drove on, she leaned forward into the seat showing off her tits. As helmeted bicyclists rode past in slow procession, blowing whistles and flipping off traffic, Angelica summarized for me her recent past—the auditions, the bartending, the illness of her kitty cat. Occasionally, I caught a whiff of perfume, when she pressed her body up against my neck and grazed the side of my face with her hair.

"Hey, I called you. Twice," I said. "Once I got your machine and the other time some guy answered. I left my number. Is that your boyfriend?"

"No," she laughed. "He's just a friend." I'm thinking, *Yeah, right.* "Someone I know from Hawaii. He was my houseguest for a month. He wanted to have a relationship with me, but I wasn't interested. He didn't give me any of your messages." There was a pause. "It was platonic. He slept on the couch."

We reached her building in Cole Valley, lush with overhanging trees and serene sidewalks. I pulled up slowly and parked in someone's driveway.

"Can we talk for a minute?" she asked, as she paid the fare.

"Sure," I said, and shut off the engine. When I turned around our eyes met, the sexual rope was taut—we started kissing. After a long, gorgeous kiss, she tapped the seat and said, "You should be back here."

"Good idea," I said, but didn't move. She moved her tongue seductively and said, "C'mon, baby."

Soon I was sitting next to her with my pants down around my ankles, rock hard. She grabbed my dick and started sucking. After awhile, she came up for air and said, "This is crazy. I probably shouldn't be doing this."

"Baby, you're doin' great. Keep going. You're doing absolutely the right thing. Just keep on..."

She turned her mouth into a fabulous o-ring and kept slurping. Sometimes, people would pass by—a guy walking his dog, a couple laughing at something the other had said. After about ten minutes, she said, "My neck is killing me. Let's go upstairs. I want you to fuck me."

"Let's fuck right here," I said, pulling down her jeans and almost ripping apart her panties.

"Don't!" she said, sounding upset. "I'm not comfortable with this. Not here!"

I figure, if I go upstairs the rest of the night is shot. Plus, if I leave the cab in the driveway, even for a quickie, it will probably be gone or have its front wheels hoisted to a tow truck when I get down. Somehow, I made her see the realities I was faced with.

On Monday night, I went back with a bottle of wine, a red rose, and some sticky green. In the fury of salsa music, we flipped the script.

This Ain't Nothing Nice

VI. (C) Duties and Responsibilities
2. No driver shall drive, or permit to be driven, a taxicab vehicle which interior is not kept clean, orderly and free of offensive odors.

When one thinks of clashes in a taxicab, what comes to mind is a fist fight, a heated debate, or a venomous silence, bubbling and troubling into clipped dialogue. However, a subtler form of conflict can go on in a taxi, involving the nose in a non-stop, unstoppered, trench-warfare of smells.

This ain't nothing nice…

One Halloween night, I had a vampire from the Exotic Erotic Ball barf all over my back seat and bolt before I knew what had happened. Then, ten years later, I had two chicks double-barf, hurling their cookies within seconds of each other.[10] I've had infants soil their Pampers and little kids shit their pants in my laboratory for human development. I've had people of both sexes, who seemed perfectly normal and worthy of respect—fill the cab with a stench that, to quote the Bard, "all the perfumes of Arabia could not sweeten." I've had a beautiful woman, sloshed to the gills, release a twenty-one-gun salute of beer farts. And a guy in a blue serge suit leave a wet ass-print that cost me forty

[10] I've only had three people get sick in my cab in my twenty-plus years of driving. As soon as someone's head starts drooping, and it looks to me like they're getting sick, there's no discussion. They're out.

The double-barf incident took place near Lake Merritt in Oakland. It's a story definitely worth telling—but not here.

bucks—twenty in supplies and twenty to pay some homeless guy to put on plastic gloves and clean the spot.

Like I said, this ain't nothing nice.

Employing the strategy that "the best defense against an offensive smell is a good smell," I have observed cab drivers the world over hanging functional little talismans from their rearview mirrors. Cardboard pine trees, plastic disks, aerosol cans, sticks of incense, fragrant oils, colognes and uplifting resins—all work to ward off the overpowering evil of smelly-ass muthafuckas ruining your shift.

That's why I could kick myself when I took the order to pick up Stinky—remembering too late what I was in for. Stinky was a blind man around retirement age with a penchant for the sauce, who apparently had had more than his share of mishaps on the way to the john. In fact, judging by the odor he gave off, he had a fuck-the-john-I'll-hold-my-ground-and-pass-my-water-here-thankyouverymuch attitude.

Convenient for him maybe…

He operated a newspaper kiosk at the corner of Geary & Larkin and opened up around 5 A.M., when the first newspaper trucks kamikaze around corners. Because he was blind and had to go down a flight of stairs, it was necessary for the driver to help him. In fact, if you chose to merely stand back and coach him, "Hand on the banister, now step down…," he'd hold out his arm and say, "No, I need you." Meaning, he would seize your forearm in his clammy hands and move slowly like a drunken debutante toward the cab. Freeing yourself from his clutches was a momentary happiness.

Inside the cab, he'd have you lowering windows as an involuntary reflex. You'd be driving along in a rain or hailstorm with all the windows at half-mast like a National Day of Mourning.

And if he asked you to close them, you'd say, "What, I can't hear you…"

"I said, roll up the windows I'm getting wet!"

"What? Speak real loud if you want me to hear you."

"I said—"

"Who said—?"

"I said, roll up—"

"A fat one and pass it around—What?"

Incontinence is certainly no laughing matter. Ask any cab driver with a full bladder hunting around for an accessible restroom. Neither is constipation. I once picked up a guy at Franklin Hospital who told me he had not had a bowel movement in five days. The expression on his face said it all.

Which brings me to Alrick,[11] a guy synonymous with the phrase "Thank heaven for automatic windows." Alrick was one of these big fish in a small pond types who thought he deserved the red carpet treatment.

He owned a bar in the Tenderloin frequented mostly by over-the-hill queens and retread Midnight Cowboy derelicts. When anyone made his acquaintance, the first words out his mouth were, "I own this bar…," as if that should make you green with envy.

He had to sit in the front seat. He was a big man with an enormous beer gut and, of course, he was foul-smelling and reeked. What he lacked in Stinky's genius for transubstantiating urine, he more than made up for by coughing non-stop into his hand. The fat, red paw he put over his mouth to block the sputum was a leaky vessel. It often happened that fluids, buried deep

---

[11] Thinking of Alrick, the real person, I intentionally chose his name with Bob, the fertilizer salesman.

in his lungs, came peekabooing through his fingers and with them, a fine spritz of pathogenic bacteria floated in your direction like a swarm of mosquitoes. This S.O.B. was the Johnny Appleseed of TB. He made you think he was special, all right. You wished you had special biohazard gear, just for him.

Comfortably riding shotgun, he would make a few leading remarks of a sexual nature, which, once swatted down, would send the conversation off in a safer direction. He liked to talk about his emphysema. "This emphysema's getting worse," he'd say in a hoarse voice.

"Yeah, I can see that."

"Funny thing is, I still can't quit smokin'."

Our history together consisted of three trips. The first was unavoidable. The other two were accidents. Once, forgetting where he lived, I picked him up at his home. Another time—the last time—I found him in a different bar in a different part of town. I pulled back a Naugahyde curtain to yell "Taxi!" when, lo and behold, I stood face to face with Alrick.

He had lost a lot of weight and there was a blue tint to his skin. It was evident he was dying. If anything, his cough had gotten worse. He told me he had a cold and asked if I would roll up the windows. This I could not do, nor could I ride roughshod over a man in his condition. What followed was a sort of chess match.

He'd want his window up, so I'd lower mine and put down the ones in the back—slyly, by increments. He'd say he felt a draft and ask me to roll up the windows.

"I have to have some air circulating, Alrick. You're coughing all over the place..."

"Yeah, but I'm sick, I have emphysema..."

"All the more reason..."

"Yes, but I'm sick with a cold!"

"I don't care. It's not very considerate. Think about the other guy for once, would ya?"

There was a long silence. The words shimmered around us. I thought about how easily my point could have been reversed. He was an old man. His lips were trembling. He lived in the same house he grew up in as a boy, at 25th & Pennsylvania on the back-end of Potrero Hill...

As we neared his place, he said, "Heard the news? Magic Johnson has AIDS."

"I heard." And I felt the Aeolian vibration move through me. Another fighter has come forward to do battle with AIDS...But Alrick broke the spell.

"He's a Big Spook! I wonder who corn-holed him."

"Colonel Sanders," I said, irritably.

"Colonel Sanders... That's funny."

"Man, why don't you take the bus..."

"What right do you have telling me to take the bus?" His lips were turning purple. "I'm a paying customer!"

"Then pay, goddamit! We're here."

He had one of those coin purses shaped like a flattened egg. Huffing and puffing, he went to great pains to mete out the exact change and stiff me on the tip. Then he threatened to have me fired, which I knew he couldn't do.

Driving away, I thought about the old, dying man, Alrick. I felt faint stirrings of sadness and fear, the horrible scenario of what could easily turn out to be my life, growing old and infirm without money in a big city. In my mind's eye, I saw the old lady with translucent skin and the hospital bracelet still on, the AIDS patient paying his fare slowly with Para-transit scrip.[12] I prompted

---

[12] Script issued by the city as supplemental income.

myself not to go there, to fight against thoughts that would worry and defeat me.

At the railroad crossing at 16th & 7th where 280 bends overhead, there are these massive columns with the girth of Sequoias. A subterranean Parthenon, they hold up the freeway and have, in their pseudo-sacred mystery, the stillness of a grove. I pump up the music for you—daughters of the urban requiem, and gun it over to a club called Mars, where a mob of people are jumping up and down waving their hands, happy as hell to see me.

Hatred

"...the language of the unheard."

—MARTIN LUTHER KING JR.

"I'm drunk... Is that okay?"

He was a tall, lean, Clint Eastwood type, early forties, with blond, hairy arms and a head showing traces of gray. He came stumbling out of La Rocca's, a famed watering hole in North Beach, late one Sunday afternoon.

"Driver, what's your name?"

I say Sean,[13] which is my cab driving persona. Cab drivers, like strippers, invent new names, as a buffer against intrusive people.

"Irish?"

"No, human." Remember, he's drunk.

"Sean, my name is Kevin. And that's the only thing Irish about me too."

He's going to the Sunset district. And I can tell he's gonna bang his gums all the way across town.

"I'm American too. I hate all this African-American, Chinese-American bullshit! If you're living in America, you're American god dammit! Don't you agree with me, Sean?" Experience has taught me never to argue with a drunk. "Isn't that what this country is all about? When you travel in a foreign country, they call

[13] "Sean" is a sort of tribute in memory of my one-time best friend, John O'Sullivan, who died in a car accident on the Bronx River Parkway, 3-24-68.

you an American, not a black, or a Greek, or what have you..."

I can tell where this is going. Bigots get in the cab, start spewing hate and try to co-opt you. Make you a silent partner.

"The problem is the media... They're manipulating us, night and day, telling us what to buy and what to think..."

"I'm with you on that Kevin..."

"Look at what they make us watch. Rosanne Barr, Jerry Seinfeld...Everything is Jewish. The Jews control the media..."

"You really think so?"

"Sean, I know so. But if you say anything, if you speak out and tell the truth, they'll label you an anti-Semite, and hound you till you lose your job. That's what they did to—the name just went out of my head, Congressman from San Mateo. They got him thrown out of office. And do you know what his crime was? He refused to recognize the State of Israel! He said that the land belonged to the Palestinians! That was his crime!"

"First of all," I said, with a deep sigh, "nobody's making you watch those shows. And secondly, Jews, as in A Zionist Conspiracy, don't control the media..."

"You know who Michael Eisner is?"

We were now in the Panhandle, leading into Golden Gate Park. It was dusk, growing darker. To our left, a cool breeze gently rattled the eucalyptus leaves, an elegant row of peeling bark and white skin, a gorgeous striptease.

"Eisner, Disney, so what? So what if there are Jews in prominent positions in the media? Do you think that adds up to them controlling how you think?"

"Sean, you're very naïve. Don't tell me they have you believin' the propaganda! Man, wake up! Do you remember the Gulf War...We fought that war for Israel..."

"Bullshit. We fought that war for oil...We fought that war for

Bush and Getty...the greedy, rich bastards, sitting on the board of directors of Shell and Chevron and Arco...We fought to keep the one percent—which controls over fifty percent of the capital in this country—secure."

I felt myself tensing up.

Kevin leaned forward and put his blond paw on the seat next to my headrest. "Sean, you really need to read up on things. Do you know that, during the Gulf War, we gave Israel 15 billion dollars—15 billion, Sean, and they didn't even fight. We gave them the money to build settlements for the Russian Jews! How 'bout buildin' houses for the Viet Nam vets...Charity begins at home, Sean..."

"Israel didn't fight because our government begged them not to. They didn't retaliate when Iraq was lobbing those scuds because the U.S. wanted to preserve its fragile alliance with Egypt and the Saudis. And yeah, they made a deal."

"Why do you think the Arabs hate this country...Why do you think they want to bomb us...It's because of the Jews...The U.S. is a puppet for Israel!"

"Israel is a tiny nation. The United States is the most powerful nation on earth. How do you arrive at your logic?"

"It doesn't matter how small Israel is, the Jews control the media, the stock market and the banks. They formulate policy by making you think pro-Israel."

"I think the opposite is closer to the truth! Israel is a key military base! It's central to U.S military strategy in the Middle East, that's why this country gives so much money to Israel. Look, I'm not an apologist for Israel and I'm not saying she's unblemished and pure, but show me a nation that is! My whole point being, it's ridiculous for you to say the Jews and Israel control the U.S."

"Okay, who's got the biggest lobby in Congress? Israel!"

"I don't know whether that's true. I'd bet that the A.M.A. and the tobacco lobbies were bigger..."

"You're wrong, Sean. The Jews don't only control money in the U.S. The Rothchilds control the world, Sean...The whole world is under the domination of a Zionist cabal! Ever hear of the Tri-lateral commission? That's the Jews, Sean! Smell the coffee!"

At the Shell Station at 7th & Lincoln, with its bright dazzle of snack food, displayed behind thick, bulletproof glass, I considered throwing him out of the cab. Kicking people out of the cab is a kind of exorcism and I would have liked to be purged of this negativity. But kicking him out would have cheated me out of the bulk of my fare and this argument could've easily erupted into a fistfight. Plus, since he looked like Mark Fuhrman with that above-the-law cockiness, I had a strong suspicion Kevin was a cop.

"George Burns, Jack Benny...Do you know that they were Jews?"

"Yeah. So what?"

"Jews are very deceptive, very sneaky. They try to disguise who they are by changing their names. I would never change my name. I'm proud of my name. You wouldn't change your name, would you, Sean?"

I could picture the old footage out of Nazi Germany. The word "Juden" and the Star of David, painted on the sunny, German walls. The Jewish shops, looted. Windows smashed. The beginning of the terror.

"Divide and conquer," Kevin snarled. "That's exactly the Jewish strategy. I don't see why a black man and a white man can't sit at bar and have a drink and get along... But the media doesn't want that! I mean, why do you think the Jews get kicked out of every country they've ever been in?"

Buona Sera...This is Ezra Pound broadcasting live from Rome...

"The Jews are such a small minority," I explained. "They're an easy target to hate!"

"They got kicked out of Hungary, Germany, etc., I'm not saying that what Hitler did was right, but, hey, the Gulf War taught me a lesson. We fought that war for the Jews. We lost 208 American lives to protect the Jews. Believe me, they'll have ice hockey in Hell before I send a son of mine to fight in a war that's sponsored by the media!"

At 32nd and Noriega, in a misty fog, Kevin came around my window to pay. A cop car pulled up to an intersection across the street and honked at him. He waved at the cruiser and offered to shake my hand. For a moment, I hesitated, before grabbing his forearm and pulling him closer.

"Kevin, what comes around goes around...Do you believe that?"

"Definitely..."

"Well, then, I hope for your sake—and the sake of the world—you come back in your next life as a Jew."

Drunken Kevin stood there looking at me with uncomprehending disbelief. A car with an orange Phillips 76 ball bobbing on the antenna stopped for the sign and pulled away behind him.

"In fact," I said, "I know for sure that this is going to happen! Know why?" He continued to fix me with his blank stare. "Because I'm a Jew. And we both know that Jews control the world!"

CODA

Sometime shortly after this, I got this couple from Israel in the cab. "I can tell you're from Israel," I said and they were astonished (and slightly paranoid) about how I knew this. "It's the accent. The way you speak English!" Remembering the thing with Kevin,

I told them right away that I was Jewish, expecting them to be delighted.

The guy says, "Unless you're practicing Judaism, you're not Jewish."

See that. If I'd had Kevin's cell phone, I could've called him and said, "Yo dawg, (I mean shfine hoont), this is Sean... Remember? The Jew from the cab...Hey, Kevin, there's been some mistake. Guess what? I'm not a Jew after all."

Cab Driving is an Addiction

For Kenny McElroy

Columbus Ave is a two-lane street. In front of Bimbo's nightclub, a bevy of Cindy-rellas are waving and jumping up and down excitedly. A stretch-limo—a preposterously long and ridiculous Hummer—blocks the entire right lane. There's a cop behind me, so I hand-signal the girls to meet me around front. Before they get in, someone pokes her head in the window. "How many will you take?"

"Five, max."

"Okay…" she says and they try to squeeze in six.

"Whoa, slow down … I'm counting…five, six."

"It's only one extra. Please…we'll give you a big tip…"

"No can do…"

"Pleeeeease…"

"Hon, it ain't gonna happen. I'm not about to waive my insurance and that's what I'd be doing if I took six."

"C'mon, please…the cab driver who took us here did it…"

"Good for him. You should have told him to pick you up."

"Forget it," a disgruntled voice from outside says.

"This guy's a jerk."

"I'm a jerk? This whole damn thing was an exercise in futility. You wasted my time and yours…"

As they file out, grumbling, I say to these fair damsels of privilege, "What a bunch of losers..." Something they probably haven't heard too much in their lives.

"Screw you," the bigmouth says. "You're the loser. Look at what you do..."

"Yeah, I drive a cab. I enlighten people."

Cab driving is a noble profession...

Nah, fuck that. Stuff that self-righteous hooey right up your exhaust pipe. *Cab driving is an addiction...*And you know it!

When you say, "I'm too old, I've been in the game too long, what else can I do?" what you're really saying is, "I'm an addict. And I'm hooked on the unbelievable straitjacket of this suffering."

When you say, "No way could I go back to a straight job... some half-ass boss standing over my shoulder telling me what to do," what you're really saying is, "I'm an addict. And I'm hooked on the preposterous limitations of this thing I mistakenly call freedom."

When you say, "I'm young, I got plenty of time...I like goin' to work broke and comin' home with some guilders in my pocket," what you're really saying is, "I can't see the hole I'm digging for myself!"

I was there. I was you...tantalized by the boho opportunities—getting high and fucking married women you meet in the cab, in the late afternoon when the honey-light pours through the windows.

I know the pleasure, and I know the pain of this job. I know what it is to feel the juice on a weekend night when it's really busy and the tension is as palpable as a balled-up fist and the electricity of the city enters your blood and its vast mega-wattage stokes the neon vasculature of your heart with a mad desire to rule and make money—I know that shit. The rush of getting out there and hustling, moving so fucking fast every move is a karate kata... Clip, clip, clip...The cowboy trip of the road is an eleven-hour catharsis. And when it's all over, and you're relaxed, counting your money in the driver's room, you might even fool yourself into thinking, "This ain't half-bad. I could live with this..."

Yeah, okay...when you start thinking like that, remember the immortal words of Bing, the gas/man, when I said to him over two decades ago, "This is only an in-between gig...Six months, a year from now, I'm gone."

Bing looked me up and down, and puffing calmly on his pipe, he replied, "That's what they all say. I'll see your ass around here twenty years from now and you'll still be talkin' that same shit."

Cab Lot-Camelot/SFO

"So tired I sleep in cab like dog. I don't need sleep in cab... I have house for sleep."

—A RUSSIAN DRIVER

The woman said she was smuggling videos into Mexico and each unwieldy duffel bag you lugged from her doorstep to the cab weighed a ton—exactly one hundred pounds, according to her. For this, she tipped you five bucks a bag. You're such an easy whore—and a fool too, because you wound up wrenching your lower back and the chiropractor is sixty bucks a visit.

Next day, walking up Kearny Street rubbing your coccyx, you pass a famous sex emporium, and think—why not? When your life is going nowhere, you can afford these diversions. Who knows? Maybe you'll get lucky and see Brigitte Bardot going down on Ava Gardner. You enter, and descend a flight of stairs into the cavernous gloom. You flick a tissue off one of the metal boxes attached along the walls and, with pincered fingers, delicately open the door to your booth. Underfoot, the floor is slippery. Your sneakers are ruined. The place reeks—micro-organisms marinating in disinfectant. "Touch me and you'll regret it!" say the walls.

You stand in pitch darkness before a blacked-out window, one slot for quarters, one for bills. You swim in your own spiritual abyss, fishing in your pocket for change. What are you doing here? Oh yeah, that's right. You're doing research—anthropological work of a highly abstruse nature. The man in the next booth...He's snug inside a porous fantasy, scuffing his shoes against the wall, talking to a succubus in hushed tones. What is he saying? Shall we invent his dialogue? Never mind that—why are you rubbing your eyes?! Alarmed, you make a beeline for the bathroom where the need to wash your hands and bathe your eyes is a desperate purification rite. The water trickling out of either tap is cold and, naturally, they're out of soap. You dry your hands on your shirt.

Leaving the bathroom, you encounter the jiz-man, an old, stooped Chinese fellow, toiling away, swabbing out niches with a mop and a bucket of suds.

"Got change?" you say, producing a twenty. He smiles, minus a few teeth, and says, "No changey...Machiney in front..."

Back in the booth, quarter in the slot, up shoots your window. Damn...Four of the skankiest women you have ever seen—some with blotchy faces,, some with pallid skin covered in tattoos—sashay around in high heels and skimpy lingerie. They go through the standard stripper drill of beaver shots and twirls (in this case, sans pole). They cavort and joke among themselves in a red-carpeted terrarium. Inconsequential men (you!) peer out at them through portholes. The very subtle contempt—cycling back and forth from you to them, a strange balance of boredom and despair—makes fascinating theatre.

Your back is killing you.

You push open the door with your foot and look through the underground gloom. The saddest light you have ever seen floods the lobby with its unworldly pain. Tilting backwards in time on the fulcrum of some unbearable childhood trauma, you feel an uncontrollable urge to escape the inescapable.

Death... Stagnation... Unseasonable humidity...

You wake up…

Welcome. It's summertime in the airport lot! Naptime is over and now you have to scrape yourself off the filthy upholstery of your taxi. Before sitting up, you roll over and see a ceiling gone brown from nicotine. On the floor next to you is *Moby Dick* by Herman Melville—you are, after all, a literary artist. But Melville would never have read *What Color Is Your Parachute?* and that's what you've been dragging around with you inside your backpack. Cut yourself some slack. It's a different world. You sit up, yawning. Before you dances a mirage of heat. The driver in front of you is running his engine. In the blue fumes of deleterious exhaust, you see all the signs of a bleak future.

Some drivers are playing cards. Some are reading. Some are laughing. Some are standing around doing nothing, enduring the wait, yakking in native tongues—English, Vietnamese, Arabic, Russian, Hindi, Portuguese, Farsi, Chinese—you hear them all as the Tower of Babel collapses in your head and someone yells, "It's moving…"

The delayed East Coast flights are in. The cabs lined up in long motionless columns—all colors, but mostly yellow—start filing out, slowly at first. A bell sounds. A whistle blows. A mad honking ensues. Cooped up, half-crazed drivers closest to the exit start screaming, "Go, Go…" The starter in uniform is screaming "Go, Go… Move it. Hurry-the-fuck up!"

But you can't go! The cab in front of you running its engine has got no driver. He's blocking the line. "Go around him!" The starter booms in a commanding voice and windmills her arm. Another driver, quick on the uptake, moves the offending cab against the wall in a tight-squeeze of punishment. It's moving now…really moving, heating up—fast and furious.

Caught lagging, drivers scramble for their vehicles, a mad dash from the piss-house or the lunch-wagon, cheesecake falling off the plate. A card game a few cab lines away vanishes. The cabs behind me, burnished under harsh light, are in state of battle readiness.

"Go!!!" The starter yells, for the second time in thirty seconds. This is the inevitable juggernaut, the sought-after effect. Lines rearranging in a rolling continuum of falling dominoes, scrambling patterns at warp speed.

Keep your eye on the one in front of you. Note his color and number. He's the one you'll follow through the maze of stop-and-go sequences. He's your bellwether.

You leave the lot. You merge. You swoop down ramp and rise, and appear at the terminal, praying under your breath with a vicious intensity, "Please, not a short...not a short!

And what do you get?

Murphy's Law!—You saw the golf clubs. They always presage disaster. Millbrae. Burlingame. San Mateo. Not far enough away to make money, but far enough into the hills to make getting back in the allotted time of thirty minutes intensely nerve-racking. So nerve-racking that you've made it back in twenty-nine minutes. And now the real torture begins. You have to wait in line behind three other cabs at the automatic ticket booth; waiting, while the long wooden arm rises and falls in a slow monotony that's killing you. Honking, cursing, leaning on the horn—it does no good, but you do it anyway, because you are a cabdriver, half-crazed, at the mercy of ruthless emotions. When you get there and grab your ticket, stamped with the time, you groan out loud because you're one minute late! Meaning, you have to go all the way back to the end of the line! Do the whole thing again from scratch—that vigil in the snake pit lasting hours! You're not gonna do that again, are you? Hell, no. So you find a guy in the lot who arrived ahead of you. You trade tickets. No sweat off his back, he's cool. And you get right back in the short line. A bell rings. The starter starts windmilling like mad...

And then it's deja-vu all over again. You're at Arrivals, observing the people as they come out and reading destinations in their luggage. Praying under your breath with a vicious intensity, "Please, not a short...not a short!"

Lusty Lady Jam

Note: If you have no stomach for Rabelaisian humor, do not read this story. Go directly to "The Cadillac of Penis Pumps."

Cabdrivers and strippers—there are odd parallels and legitimate comparisons. Strippers make a lot more money in a lot less time than cabdrivers. But in the eyes of society, both are marginalized, dead-end gigs. Neither scores points on a résumé. You're never going to hear, "You drove a taxi for five years? Plus, you lived with a stripper? We've been looking for that kind of off-the-wall experience. You're hired! When can you start?" And yet, in both professions, even when our self-esteem is challenged daily, we serve the priestly function of compassionate listener and psychotherapist. The patience and tolerance we develop for "assholes" allows us to accept the very worst in human behavior with a shrug.

Strippers have told me some wild stories. A visiting starlet at "The New Century" with big collagen lips and fake hooters told me she had a regular who used to give her $50 apiece for new panties. She'd buy cheap $3.00 underwear at a discount store and turn a nifty $47.00 profit on each item. "He'd buy ten at a time!" she enthused.

In the early '80s when Japan's economy was on top, another stripper told me about her Japanese sugahdaddy with money to burn. "He was a freak for blonde pubic hair," she said. "And even though I was a brunette, wearing a blonde wig when I met him, I didn't let that stop me." With a little Clairol and a lot of American know-how, she FedExed him a monthly quota of golden pubes in a small lacquered box he gave her expressly for that purpose. She was paid according to the number of hairs, a situation that soon lead to the total deforestation of her pussy. But once again she proved equal to the entrepreneurial challenge and began buying and chopping up blond wigs...made in China.

I was talking to one of the dancers at the *Lusty Lady* one night as I was driving her to work. She made her living sitting naked—sometimes spread-eagled—behind a windowed partition, watching yo-yos shoot cum shots on the transparency that separates them. Taking a cue from my passengers, I asked her, "What's the sickest, most depraved thing you've ever seen on the job?" She giggled, and told me about a pervert of mythological stature, who pays girls to watch him lick piping hot semen (and maybe even a few fly heads) off the window. As soon as an ejaculator leaves the booth, in pops this "connoisseur of cum" for his little treat.

"Tell me it's not true!" I pleaded.

"You asked for it!"

"That's pretty hard to swallow..."

"At least it's organic..." she replied.

"So, as a connoisseur, do you think he said things like 'Let it breathe. It gets better the longer it drips...' "

"Ooo...that is *so* disgusting."

"Even now, in my mind's eye, I can see him savoring each little pearl drop, perhaps swirling some of the nectar over his tongue the better to identify the bite. Praising the bouquet..." I paused to see if she was still with me.

"You...Are...Sick!"

"What are you talkin' about. It's your story!"

She was a little Latina firecracker, early-to-mid-twenties, wearing a lacy bra and showing a lot of tit. The ends of her blouse were tied in front, revealing the sweetest little navel ring.

"Tonight the club was crawling with fags," she said.

"What are gays doing in a straight strip club? " I asked, fascinated by the anomaly. We were heading up Franklin past the ornate gilt dome of City Hall, making all the lights.

"When I first started, I wondered the same thing," she said, honking her nose and apologizing for her cold. "They go in there to cruise for horny guys."

"You see, now, that's the kind of valuable information I'm looking for."

"At least the fags use condoms! It's the closet fags, the ones who are scared to death that someone will see them...They're the ones having unprotected sex." During the day, she told me, she counseled teens dealing with HIV and hepatitis C.

She was going to Broadway & Kearney, to Enrico's for some soup. For the rest of the ride, she flew into a tirade about AIDS. "AIDS is serious shit, but people don't want to hear about it anymore. It's yesterday's news. But did you know that ten percent of South African youth, between the ages of 15 to 25, are infected with HIV? And of that ten percent, 77% are women my age! And they can't even get anti-viral drugs to those people because that government is so far behind the learning curve."

When I dropped her off, watching her lovely ass disappear into the crowd that was standing in front of Enrico's, I thought—some lucky guy is gonna be hittin' that. And I also thought, if this world is ever gonna be saved from the plague of greed, anger and stupidity that so dominates us at present, it'll be saved by people like her. Young people who know the world and its weird nuances of brutality and ugliness: beautiful people like her.

On my way home from work that night, under the mistaken impression that I was sharing something novel, I told my buddy, Dimitri, about "the connoisseur of cum." After going through the expected facial contortions, he said, "When I was mixing concrete in the Mission for my uncle, I got friendly with this Capp Street hoe. She used to save used condoms for a guy who would drink them…"

The following day, I told the same story to my 500 lb. cab-driving buddy, Big John, on our way to work.

"Yeah, that's like the story of Smokey's milkshake," John laughed. "Back when I was a kid, drivin' cab in LA, I knew this hooker who got real pissed off at her old man for cheatin' on her. To get back at him, she collected a batch of used condoms—tied 'em up with her teeth—and emptied the whole thing in a MacDonald's milkshake. She gave it to ole Smokey to drink. A few days later, when there was about 500 miles between them, she phoned in the news.

"Smokey's milkshake!" Big John laughed, earthquaking at his own joke.

The Cadillac of Penis Pumps

"When in doubt, tell the truth..."

—MARK TWAIN

Saturday night 3:00 A.M., the flesh trade is in high gear. I ring the doorbell of a massage parlor in the Tenderloin. A young Asian chick pokes her pretty head out the door. Then, half-revealed in the light, she waves from behind a locked metal gate, saying, "Will coming soon..."

Thirty seconds later...

An old fart, straight out of a vintage Playboy cartoon, stands between doorway and gate, basking in the warm send-off of two young masseuse-whores in silk kimonos. Strands of disheveled hair stick out in all directions and his pink face is flushed with the kind of excitement that bespeaks manly triumph.

"We make massagey again," one of the girls giggled. Her friend straightened the man's collar. It was a very cold night but he was standing there half-dressed: coat wide open, shirt half-buttoned, belt unbuckled and hanging limply off his waist. They got his money. Now they were getting rid of him—gently, gently pointing him towards me, ushering him into the street with a splendid farewell. He must have dropped a bundle—only big money induces this kind of fawning, ass-kissing enthusiasm.

In the cab, he smiled like the cat that ate the canary and said, "I just fucked the shit out of both them little gals."

"Judging by that send-off, you must have really put the wood to 'em."

"Brother, did I ever..." he said, beaming with pride—matting down the remaining few wisps of white hair that feathered his skull. He was going to the Marriott at the airport, a good load.[14]

"Trouble is..." he said, grunting like a guy trying to pass a basketball through his anus. "For fifteen years, I couldn't get it up. Now, I can't get the goddamn thing *down!*"

"Huh?"

"I said, for fifteen years...*agh*, mother of God, this thing hurts!"

"What exactly are we talking about?"

"Ah, hell's bells. We are talking about my dick."

"Why are we talking about your dick?"

"Because it's stuck. My penis pump is stuck!"

He told me that the blight of impotency, which had cast a black cloud over his life for the last fifteen years, had suddenly lifted two days ago, when he had a prosthetic penis put in.

"This shouldn't be happening. With a cheaper model, yes, maybe...but not with this puppy! What I've got here is the very best pump made anywhere in the world today. Top of the line. My doctor calls it the 'Cadillac of Penis Pumps.'"

"But it's not working?"

"Oh, it's working all right. Too fucking *well!*"

"But it's malfunctioning? It's stuck?"

"*Stuck on Fuck,* yeah. And hurts like all-get-out too..."

"Like the dickens, huh?"

"You betchya. Very, very uncomfortable," he said, making a face and pushing down forcefully on the boing-boing, jack-in-the-box contrap in his lap. "I felt like Superman in there, kid.

---

[14] In the context of this story, "load" could be interpreted in a very different way. But, in San Francisco cab jargon, the word "load" is synonymous with the word "ride."

Three straight hours with a lead pipe hard-on."

"I hate it when that happens..." I said with an eye-roll.

"Like a fucking teenager, I was. A fucking tiger."

"You found the fountain of youth."

"Yessiree, Bob! I couldn't get it up. Now I can't get it down!" he half-chuckled. "That's my new slogan, buddy boy: I couldn't get it up, now I can't get it down."

"That's pretty funny."

"Yeah, for you maybe. But for me, this is no laughing matter. My doctor told me to consider it a medical emergency if I stayed hard for over three hours. And we're closing in on..." he consulted his watch, ...four right now. Is there a hospital nearby?"

"A hospital?" I asked, a few blocks from the freeway.

"They have medicine for this condition. Something to constrict the arteries."

I'm thinking, Shit! I'm gonna lose this airport run. Less concerned with his penis than my fare, I tried to reason with him. "The only problem with the hospital is, you're gonna wait a long time before anyone sees you. You know that, right? And then after they see you, they're gonna charge you an arm and a leg for your penis... Sorry, I shouldn't be joking about this..."

"No, no... Believe me, the humor is not lost on me either."

"I'm just making the point," I said. "The nearest hospital, St. Francis, is very expensive."

"I know," he said. "I know all about the cost...But I think, considering the possibility of irreparable damage, I should go anyway..."

"This may sound stupid," I said, "but why not try a bag of ice. That'll constrict the arteries, won't it?"

"I don't know," he said. "This is potentially very dangerous. There are thousands of delicate little veins in the penis. If you damage them, you're done. Or, more precisely, I'm done. No more erections, no more massage girls, no more superman heroics... No more sex, *ever!*—that's what the urologist said."

"Wha'd the proctologist say?"

"None of his fucking business. Let's stop somewhere and buy a bag of ice."

"Sure, absolutely. I think this will work."

"I hope so. Gotta do something. This bastard is killing me."

"Yeah. Let's put some ice on that bad boy." I'm thinking, Man, am I a cold sonofabitch, or what?

At a bodega at 7th & Mission, just before hopping on the freeway, I bought him a seven-pound bag of ice with a blue polar bear mugging on the package. He put it on his incorrigible laptop like a sorta man-made avalanche.

"How does that feel?"

"Cold...cold as a witch's tit."

"Besides that..."

"I don't know. It still hurts."

"Give it about fifteen minutes. Icing your penis shouldn't be any different than icing your back, or your shoulder, or any other part of your body...Wouldn't you think?"

His face still wore an impossibly grim expression. To divert his mind from the pain—and satisfy my own curiosity—I asked, "How does it work, this penis pump?"

"They do what's called a prosthetic intervention. They insert two tubes and a ball valve, which is a little pump tucked away in my scrotum. When I squeeze the ball, fluid goes from the ball into the tubes and I get an erection. Squeeze it again, and it's suppose to go flaccid. In theory."

"Is this the first time you've tried it?" I asked.

"No...Hell, no!!" he cried. " I've been having sex non-stop for the last two nights. I mean, c'mon, why not? To orgy or not to orgy, there is no question!" He flashed a mouth of lewd false teeth.

A few minutes from his hotel, he told me he'd recently retired, was new to the Bay area, and didn't know a soul. "I'm moving into a beautiful fourteen-room mansion up in Hillsborough. Give me your number. When I get settled in, you can visit. And bring girls...Introduce me to some of the local talent...I've got a swimming pool. We'll have a blast. A few cocktails, then...everyone into the pool, strip naked and go wild..."

"Sure. Definitely...Here's my card for when you get settled in." I handed him a company card, which also serves as receipt, and scribbled down the name Fred Nietzsche—the first name that came to mind. A stupid, sophomoric joke.

"Call me Freddie," I said, as he slowly groaned his way out of the cab.

"Okay, take—errgh!—easy, Freddie..."

"Good luck with the ice," I said, watching him waddle into the lobby of the Airport Marriott with seven pounds of slowly melting ice between his legs. How long, I wondered, would he keep the ice in that position? Would it affect his ability to get a room? And more to the point, come morning, what scandals would he inflict on the Spanish-speaking ladies of the housekeeping staff? It was only then, after he had left the cab and these questions flashed through my mind, that I discovered a wet spot, the size of a Sumo wrestler's ass, on the velour upholstery of my Dodge Intrepid.

It poses a unique dilemma: What do I do? Cover it with a towel, assuming I had a towel to cover it with? And furthermore, what do I tell the next passenger, when she sees a towel on the seat?

Certainly not the truth; nobody would ever believe that.

My Gym Bag

Most drivers won't admit it, but a single gay dude is preferable to a gaggle of drunken yuppies any day. Gays are good tippers, too. In San Francisco, we're way ahead of the game when it comes to tolerance. Whether you suck dick or eat pussy or inhale farts off bus seats, that's your business! Just show the other person a little respect, that's all anybody asks. And, for this reason, as a precaution against intrusive "front seaters," I always keep my gym bag next to me, positioned strategically, in the shotgun seat.

This one particular gay sex club had a direct line to our company. And because it was a great account—often sustaining us through the slow, pre-dawn hours—drivers were instructed, commanded, enjoined, and lectured on the importance of getting out and ringing the damn bell.

"Get out and ring" was every dispatcher's mechanical mantra. Even among lazy drivers, even in the rain—most would get out and ring, not wanting to hear the famous rant, "You guys really wanna lose the account, don't ya? The guy inside just called and gave me a haircut!"

Still, this time, I didn't feel like budging. It was no more than ten feet from the curb to a low industrial building with mirrored windows and a rainbow flag. The bell, shaped like a nubile little tit, read, "Taxi." Still, I didn't want to move. Not tonight. Tonight all I wanted was to stop this coughing. This dry, rasping, ugly cough. This cough, which, despite the Rx codeine Robitussin and the Allegra I kept stashed in my gym bag, had continued to provoke the comment, "What's with that cough?" For the past three months, it had taken to nesting deep in my lungs like a fierce bird of prey.

On top of that, I just didn't wanna deal with the crowd—a cancan line of Village People decked out in leather. The line stretched halfway around the block. I caught a glimpse of myself in the mirrored windows and didn't like what I saw. Losing weight, looking really rundown...

And that's when he came thumping out, this heavily perspiring, hairy-chested, pot-bellied queen in a leather vest. He tried the front door, but it was locked. Then he saw the leather gym bag resting next to me like an installation sculpture, flashing a great big "verboten" sign. I gave a quick stab in the air with my thumb. He got the message and climbed in the back.

"Lots of people inside waiting. You guys are gonna be busy tonight!" The people who ran this club were cool. They kept the loads inside and didn't let them wander off before we got there.

"What's all the hoopla about?" I asked.

"What do you meeean?" he slurred.

"I mean, why the flags and the big crowd?"

"Oh..." he said, "The Bears are in town."

"Which Bears, the Chicago Bears?" I wasn't joking. I didn't have a fucking clue.

"No," he chuckled. "Big, hairy, out-of-shape motherfuckers like me!"

"Oh, those bears!"

"Yeah," he grunted, reeking of poppers.

(The doctor said it was allergies. It had to be. Just last week they took a chest x-ray and it came out negative.) A cassette was playing WU-TANG FOREVER.

"Can we listen to some *MUSIC!* I hate that Rap shit!"

"Oh, you don't like WU-TANG featuring Vanilla Ice?"

"Who? I hate that Gangsta Rap shit!"

"All right, since you feel that way...I'll shut the radio off completely."

"'Mother-fuck this...Mother-fuck that...You bitch-hoe-motherfucker!' You call those lyrics?"

"Is that what you heard? Because that's not what he was saying."

"Well, that's the gist of what they say! Fuck, Fuck, Fuck...Play something else."

"We're gonna observe silence. Silence is golden." We drove on in silence with what I thought was a comfortable vibe.

Then, a few blocks later, he goes, "I'll pay to suck your dick!" I hit the brake and stopped. "Excuse me, sir...What did you say?"

"I said...Oh, it doesn't matter what I said. I'm drunk!"

"Didn't you suck enough dick for one night?" I shot back.

"Apparently not..." he said, tittering and slowly grasping the fact that we had stopped moving. I turned around and beamed on him.

"Are you gonna be nice, or am I gonna have to kick you out?" He looked drunk, sloppy drunk, which was odd, since I knew they didn't serve alcohol inside.

"I'm sorry," he said, fumbling in his pocket and handing me a scrunched-up twenty. "Here take this. I'm sorry. I'm an asshole. I truly am a sorry-ass asshole. Are you angry?"

"Not if this is a restitution payment."

"Listen to him. What do you think I am, Germany after the

First World War! Restitution payment, my ass...It's an act of good faith."

"You're givin' me this twenty on top of the meter, right? "

"Well, I don't know...Should I? What have you done for me lately? What have you done to earn it?"

"I've been biting down on my lip real hard. And to me, that means a lot. So, yeah...I've earned it!"

"Maybe you have. Maybe that's what I had in mind just now when I handed it to you."

"You're a very mysterious man. But I think you're right... *about the money...*"

"But you're still pissed at me, aren't you?"

"Not any more. You've paid your debt to society."

"Oh, please...Why don't you just punch me in the mouth and get it over with?"

He struck me as the type who'd probably get off getting popped in the face a few times. So I ignored him. We rode on in icy silence. The CHP was setting out flares around the scene of a nasty accident at Division and Harrison, shimmering bits of glass and motorcycle parts scattered over the area.

"What do you do for a living?" He had to be in his late forties, early fifties, probably a banker issuing home loans by day.

"I'd rather not go there." I caught a glimpse of him in the mirror, smelling his armpits and making a face. "But don't worry, I won't kill myself in your cab..."

"What kind of thing is that to say..?"

"It's what I feel, okay? I'm depressed, okay? Life sucks, okay?"

"You know, I'm keeping the twenty and you're still paying for this fare."

"Of course, I am. And I going to give you a big tip too."

Big tip, in its typical usage, is shorthand for a buck. But the rest of the way, I stayed studiously calm and didn't say another word. Under the serene hush of maple trees on Henry Street, he made another quick apology before tipping me three dollars, on top of the twenty and the fare.

"There… Are you happy?"

"Yeah, I'm satisfied."

"So, can I tell you why I'm being such an obnoxious asshole? In two minutes or less? I know you're a cabdriver and you're in a big rush to make money, but…can I tell you?"

"Go ahead," I said, through my dry, hacking cough. "I'm listening."

"I've been in the hospital since 4:00 A.M. this morning with my lover. Well, actually not in the hospital all that time. I took him home this morning around 8:00. His eyes were two slits and he had a big bag of ice over his face."

"Jeez, what happened?"

"We were at a party on 18th just off Castro. Some psycho-dickhead came in off the street with a fucking rifle and hit John smack in the face with the butt-end of his gun. Right in the teeth! And now he doesn't have any teeth." He glared at me.

"I'm sorry." I didn't know what else to say.

"My beautiful husband lost his beautiful smile. His face is a mess, swollen beyond belief. Reticulated with a million broken blood vessels. And you tell me—does life suck, or does life suck!!! Because the only person I have ever loved in my whole long and lonely life has not spoken a goddamn word to me, not a single word, since I brought him home early this morning."

The man was holding his head as he left the cab.

Some People Don't Deserve a Cab

Consider this a self-evident truth—*Some people don't deserve a cab!* I'm not talking about those lame-asses who don't know how to hail one—the statues who give you this idiotic, bovine stare as you roll past, hoping that your acutely sensitive ears and psychic training will pick up their message, "Hey, we want a cab."

Or, that other type—their polar opposite—the troglodytes running frantically toward you screaming, "Taxi! Taxi!!" and threatening to throw themselves under the wheels if you don't stop—in some cases, actually doing it—hurling curses, beer bottles, or just plain hurling—as you quickly pull away.

Or, how about the drug user with no cash and no collateral, who swears, "My friend is waiting outside with the money."

Or, the geniuses standing at the end of the bus line on a rainy night, bitterly complaining, "It's impossible to get a cab in this town. I've been waiting over an hour and not a single cab has passed." What do you say to this? Tomorrow, when it's sunny, try tanning with a tarp over your head!

Or, people on cell phones who don't know where the fuck they're at, and call cabs to non-existent addresses?

Or, the ones that flag cabs from the median strip and look pissed off and persecuted that no one is stopping.

Or, the asshole on the other side of the street waving madly for your cab, who gets you to pull the move of the century, crossing three lanes of traffic in a busy intersection, only to tell you as he reaches for the door, "Sorry, dude. I changed my mind."

And how 'bout them yuppies! Them yuppies who wave you down with passionate intensity and then can't get it together to find the rest of their crew, entering the cab one at a time in a torturous parade of confusion until someone realizes, "Where the fuck is Megan? We can't leave without Megan!" And they all pile out, talking real loud—four cellphones and four separate conversations—leaving you to contemplate the non-event that just happened.

Still, when I say—*Some people don't deserve a cab!*—I'm not talking about these people. I'm talking about a virulent, subspecies of imbecile. An asshole with so little self-control that wearing a colostomy bag over his head probably wouldn't help. (But it wouldn't hurt either.)

I'm talking about a guy named Seamus (aka Shamus) and his two inebriated friends, a trio I picked up at a bar in the Richmond called the Abbey Tavern.

"Two more comin'," says the Irishman who plops into the shotgun seat next to me.

In a gesture of forced self-restraint, I run my fingers through my hair.

"Are you a patient man, or a busy man?" the Irishman asks.

"Sometimes I'm patient, and sometimes—where are your friends?"

"You're a busy man," he says, slapping his hand on the roof in confirmation.

"I'd say I'm pretty patient, judging by what's happened so far."

"What's happened so far?"

"I've been waiting eight minutes."

"The meter's running, whudah ya karr?" says a redhead with major cleavage, who pirouettes in.

"Yeah, now it is," I say to her, "but it wasn't for a long time."

"Where are you going?"

"Sexy-one Soltane Street, Daly City." The redhead looks over her shoulder. "Where the hell is he?" Then, sticking her head out the window, she bloodcurdles, "Shamus, Shamus, goddamn you…! Hurry the fuck up, the meter is running."

"Shamus, you fucking wanker, you're costing us money, hurry up!!" Shotgun yells.

The moment Shamus staggers from the saloon, I know this is gonna be way more trouble than it was worth. Shamus looks like Mr. Clean sans the hygiene. Big, loud and mean—and very, very drunk. He probably sprinkled some leprechaun dust on the bartender, too, judging by how fast the guy shut the door and deadbolted it against re-entry. Who would have thought that walking twenty feet to a cab could turn into a journey of a thousand miles? He zigzagged forward. He *zagzigged* backwards. He staggered. He paused. He did a complete about-face and marched purposefully back to the wall of that fine establishment, where he once again paused, this time to relieve himself, recycling the beer he had quaffed in great abundance. Splattering away at 3:00 A.M. in full public view.

"What are you doing, you bollix!"

"That's the longest piss ever…

"The meter's runnin', you shite…"

"For fuck sakes, why's the meter runnin'? We ain't even started yet," Shamus says, climbing in with a visible wet spot.

Cab drivers with far less experience and a lot more sense

would have bailed by this time. But I'd decided to turn this ride into a little experiment, a test of my self-composure, if you will.

Do I sound deluded? Wait.

Anyway, it's too late. To kick them out now and call another cab would undoubtedly cause a ruckus, maybe even a fight. And to pull the key from the ignition and walk away—the best and wisest strategy—was made impossible by the fact that the ignition key (the bane of my existence all shift) was stuck in its fucking little hole like Excalibur. No amount of jiggling and cursing would get it out. So, for better or worse, these were my passengers.

"Going to Daly City, right?"

"Yes, sir," Red confirmed. "Sexy-one Soltane Street in Daly City."

"Sixty-one Soltane? I'm not sure where that is. What exit do I take?"

"Who the fuck cares? Take 'em all!" Shotgun screamed.

"No, seriously. I need an exit. I don't know where Soltane Street is."

"Take the Mission Street exit," Red said.

"Take Westlake!" Shamus screamed.

"Who the fuck cares? Take 'em all!" Says the jack-off to my right.

All this, my good reader, and I haven't even taken the car out of park yet! "Ladies and Gentleman," I announce. "I'd like everyone to agree on the exit before we get close."

"Mission Street!" the redhead yodels.

"Westlake!" Shamus growls.

"Shamus, fuck off!" Red overruled him. "Please, Mr. Taximan, take Mission. Don't listen to him. He's an asshole."

I tell them how I plan to go. "Is that cool?" I ask. No one said anything. "Since I don't hear any objections…that's how we're going."

"Captain, can we change the radio station?" Shotgun asks.

"Sure. Absolutely." I shut off the dispatch radio. "Let's just listen to music," I say. "We don't need the distracting noise."

"Captain, can we smoke?" Shotgun wants to know.

"Sorry, man. No smoking."

"No smoking?—You're not serious. You can't really be serious, are you?"

"Quite serious. This is a no-smoking cab."

"Jesus, man... You're killing me."

"I'll have you there in fifteen minutes. You can wait fifteen minutes, can't you?"

"I cannot. People become famous in less time."

"Listen to this bollix. Gimme a cigarette. I'll smoke wherever I damn well please!" Shamus says, clamping a paw on Shotgun's shoulder.

"Not in this cab. This is California," I say.

"Fuck California!! I'm not even a citizen of the United States."

"The law is on my side."

"Fuck all, you'd never get away with it where I come from. Never!"

"Shamus, shut your pie-hole," the redhead says. "It's his cab. He sets the rules."

How's your composure doing? I ask myself. Fine? Okay, cool. I start what I hope is going to be a benign topic of conversation, "I love the poets of your country..."

"Which ones?" the redhead asks.

"Yeats, Beckett, Joyce..."

"Christ, they're all dead!" she yelps.

"He's a morbid fuck, ain't he?" says Shamus, jutting his torpedo head into the front.

"I'm a poet," I hear myself saying pathetically.

"I wouldn't own up to it in public, if I were you," Shotgun says. "Hey, Captain, be a good lad. I'll hold the cigarette out the window."

"The answer is *NO.*"

"Let's hear one of your poems," Shamus says.

I recite something I know by heart, as we cut through Golden Gate Park out to 19th Ave.

"Pure bollix. I didn't fancy that at all. Let's hear another."

"Hey, you don't like it, fine. But one's all you're getting."

"I bet you don't even know three counties in Ireland. That's the trouble with you Americans. You don't know any geography and you don't care about anyone but yourselves." Shotgun wanted an argument. I turned up the radio.

"That radio is too damn loud!" Shamus says, and they all start shouting at each other in a garbled brogue.

I told myself, *chill, these are bad, but workable, conditions.* I'll just turn up my control level a notch and go into my *fast 'n' blast technique*, meaning, I crank up the music real loud and drive like a bat out of hell. Using this method I have won over many a rowdy drunk. Somebody always snaps to attention, and says, "I like the way this guy drives!"

Not this time.

"Turn that fucker down!" Shamus shouts, reaching into the front seat, where I block his arm and lower the music myself.

I turn the radio off. A welcome hiatus. They talk among themselves again.

"Here comes Mission Street!" I announce, doing my Jack in "The Shining" impression. No one says anything, not a word or a grunt or a sneeze, until we are right on top of the exit. Then Shamus lets loose the non sequitur, "John Daly Boulevard is in Westlake!" This is about as relevant as saying tuna fish is sold in cans.

"He's right," Shotgun says. "Take Westlake."

"Yeah, but what does that have to do with Soltane Street?" I ask, slowing down on the freeway, nanoseconds away from making a perilous right-angle turn.

"Sexy-one Soltane!" Red screams.

"Westlake! *Westlake!*" Shamus and Shotgun yell at the same time.

"Okay, fuck it. Westlake it is." I say, racing past the Mission Street exit.

The dildo sitting next to me has rolled down his window all the way and, with half his body projected outside into the cold air, he's yelling, "I'm gonna have a smoke. I don't give a shit what you say."

Heading toward the Westlake exit, I gun it. A mean bastard who hopes this stupid prick will fall out and split his fucking head wide open like a cantaloupe has replaced the Buddha. "Hey, buddy, cool it. I'm trying to get you home in one piece, okay?"

"I'm having a nicotine fit."

"Show some respect, man. This is a no-smoking cab. How many times do I have to say it?" Coming off the exit, there was a fork in the road.

"Go right..." says Red.

"Go left..." says Shamus.

"Go right..." says Red.

"Go left..." says Shamus.

I go right.

"Where the fuck are you going?" Shamus yells.

"I'm following your directions," I reply. "I asked you where. And no one said anything. Then she said right, and you said left, so I went right. Remember, I told you, I'm not sure where Soltane Street is." The guy having the nicotine fit turns on the radio and starts messing with the channels.

"Sexy-one Soltane!" Red yodels again.

"This is absolutely wrong!" Shamus yells in my ear.

"Listen to him. He's right!" Shotgun says.

I turned off the radio and turn the cab completely around in the opposite direction, heading into a super-thick fog. Shamus leans forward and bellows, "We're lost. And our fucking driver doesn't have a clue."

"I need directions. It's no secret."

"You're supposed to know."

"But…I don't know. I confess…I don't know where Soltane Street is. I've made that manifestly clear from the beginning."

"*Manifestly clear.* Did you hear that? He said, *Manifestly clear.* He *is* a poet!" Said the a-hole having the nicotine fit.

"Why do you need directions? You're a cab driver. You should know where you're going."

"I'm a San Francisco cab driver. This is Daly City."

"Do you have a fucking map at least?"

"Shamus, shut the fuck up," the redhead said.

"Yeah, I've got a map. But I thought that someone in this cab knew where he or she was going. I thought at least one of you knew where Soltane Street was."

"You thought wrong!" says a hard male voice.

"For the last five minutes, I've been pleading with you people for some simple cooperation. 'I need directions, I need directions.' But since I'm not getting any…"

"He's not getting any…" Shotgun says to the backseat. "That's the real problem. He's not getting any."

I hoist my gym bag out from under his legs, where it has been jammed, and pull out the *Thomas Guide for San Francisco County.*

"Just admit it, you're lost," said Shamus.

"Of course, I'm lost. That's why I'm looking at the fucking map!"

"Shut that fucking meter off then!" Shamus says. "That fucking meter should not be running while you're doing your homework. Man, you wouldn't last a day in London."

"I can't read this. The print is too small. I need better light," I say, disgusted.

"Fuck you, I'm not paying," Shamus declares.

I give no response to a threat that would normally pull the plug on any ride. Instead, I drive up half a block and stop under a streetlamp. The Buddha experiment is five minutes past failure, headed into an abyss of piss.

"I don't have a good map of Daly City." I tell them, eyes burning from a night of staring into headlights and halogens, and now the minutiae of fine squiggly lines and Lilliputian print. I scan page 18 of the Thomas Guide, a page divided and a world divided, half San Francisco / half Daly City. No Soltane Street!

"I can't find Soltane Street. It's not on the map."

"What do you mean it's not on the map? Of course, it is. We live there."

"Gimme that map book," Shamus says, grabbing for it. Calmly, I handed it over my head.

"Fucking bollix. Can't find Soltane Street," Shamus grumbles as he rifles through the pages. I shut the meter off at $19.95. "When we get there, just pay me fifteen bucks."

"Shamus, you donkey's ass! You fucking fool!" the redhead says, roaring with laughter. "What the fuck are you doing?" She ripped the map out of his hands. "He's reading the map upside down!"

"Your fucking map sucks!" Shamus yells.

"Lemme have it back," I say, receiving it stoically, and shoving it back into my gym bag. "This fog is really bad," I announce, as we roll through the opalescent psyche of a sleeping cloud.

"We'll probably get home some time tomorrow," Shamus says. "Shut that fucking meter off!"

"It is off, you asshole," Red said.

"Okay, this is going from the sublime to the ridiculous. I'm gonna call my dispatcher and ask for directions."

"Why didn't you think of that ten minutes ago?" Shotgun antes in.

"Have you got that satellite guidance thingy? " Red wanted to know. "Call your office. Have them guide us there."

"Beam me up, Scottie!" Shamus says. He had them in stitches. Convulsive laughter. Hahaha...

In the extreme fog of Daly City and Pacifica, drivers often piggyback themselves caravan-style to a lead set of taillights—usually a cab driver whose time-cooker makes him intrepid. Tonight, I'm the leader, piloting through the fog without the advantage of engaging someone else's red smudges.

"I can't see a fucking thing!" Shotgun says.

"I can't see a fucking thing!" Shamus echoes—climbing half-way into the front seat, elbows digging into my shoulder blades.

"Well, I can. So...sit back down and get your elbows out of my back."

"Shamus, for the love of Christ!" Red bloodcurdles, and hauls him into his seat.

"You don't know where the fuck you are, do you?"

"Not that shit again, please...All I wanna do is get us out of this soup without hitting anything." At which point, a pair of headlights materializes out of nowhere. I mash the brakes to avoid hitting him.

"Whiplash! Whiplash!" Shamus yells.

"You bollix, you don't even know what whiplash is," Shotgun laughed. "Look at him. The wanker's screamin' *whiplash* and holdin' his goddamn balls!"

"Fuck this cab, I'm not paying a red cent!" Shamus says, opening his door halfway. The little alarm bell goes off... ding/ding/ding...

"Shamus, you dickwad, what are you doing? You don't have a clue where you are. Not the faintest fucking clue," Red says. "Get back inside this taxi. If you get out here, you'll be lost forever."

"They'll have to send out a search party, Shamus. Dogs and all!" Shotgun quips.

"Your face will be on milk cartons all over America. And then the entire country will know you're a fucking loser," says Red.

"Fuck off, for fuck sakes, I don't karrr. I'm walkin'."

I'm not lucky enough for this to happen.

Somehow they coaxed him back in. Somehow we find Soltane Street. Somehow we get to sixty-one...or where sixty-one would have been, if it had existed.

"This is not sex-sex-one!" says Shamus.

"The address is sexy-one Soltane," Red slurs.

"It can't be," I say, pointing to an empty lot littered with broken glass and abandoned car parts. "It's not on the map. There is no sixty-one."

"Who said, sex-tee-one? It's sex-sexty one!" cried Shamus. "To hell with him, I'm not paying this wanker!"

I take the high road, continuing to ignore him and argue my case. "Soltane terminates right here..." I say, driving halfway down the deadend to illustrate my point.

"He's got us so fucking lost, I have a mind to sue."

"Shamus, fuck off...Driver, kick him out right here. He

deserves to walk all night in this soup."

I make a command decision. I am going back to the Daly City BART station. They are getting out. If a fight erupts, so be it.

And then, after I make this decision, on the other side of the boulevard, I spot my salvation—a line of cabs, six or seven deep, enticing me like a mirage. I cruise alongside the first guy in line. "Yo, buddy...You know where the six hundred block of Soltane Street is?

"Yes, I know," he says in a terse, Middle Eastern accent, lifting himself up from a slumped posture to one of active participation.

"Good, take my passengers. I can't find it."

"I take. No problem," he says, excited to inherit my ride.

"He doesn't even have a fucking map!" Shamus says, pointing at me, as they make ready to leave.

"Remember, I shut the meter off at $19.95...But because we got lost and all that, just gimme ten bucks," I say, testing my luck. To my surprise Red gives me a twenty. "Mr. Taximan, I apologize for these boys. They're drunk."

Getting rid of these people without the eruption of violence or help from the police was nothing short of a miracle. The kind of thing that makes you believe in some weird form of divine intervention. Thank you, *Saint Fiacre.* I celebrated by driving around the block and parking at a safe distance to watch the next episode unfold.

Shamus was still there where I left him—staggering around in the middle of the street. The other two were hollering the familiar refrain, "Shamus, you bollix, get in the fucking cab!"

Several of the Middle Eastern driver's friends had closed ranks around his orange cab and were in the street smoking cigarettes, enjoying the free entertainment and secretly exulting in their good fortune at not being first in line. They were like a bunch of adolescent boys about to pull a prank. *Watch this! When he steps on the gas, a cream pie the size of an airbag is going to explode in his face!* Where once stood a sleepy, dismal line of cabs, a party atmosphere now prevailed.

Even Shamus looked like he was having fun. The only one who didn't look happy was the driver. It was beginning to dawn on him that he had stepped into something nasty. His decision to scoop these people up had been a big mistake.

Thus proving another self-evident truth of the cab business, "For every asshole out there, there's a driver dumb enough to take him."

Hey, I should know.

3

THE TAO OF 4 DOORS TO THE WIND

"Just as any morning could turn lurid,

any moment could turn final,

again as in a dream."

—JOAN DIDION

Cab Driving is a Video Game

"Stupidity is the basic building block of the universe..."

—FRANK ZAPPA

cab driving is a video game
of split-second reactions
so many speeding tickets in the beginning
when the docket didn't spell my name right I got uptight
Evil Knievel on a cable-car hill
Racing/facing Alcatraz that's how we chill
throw the chassis up high playa
we get more than air we get sky playa/11-hr decathlon
raw nerves is the shit I'm on
leaning on the horn like Lena Horne tryin' to catch a break in traffic/stressed out with a pounding headache, please/I'm in a tight squeeze/I put Vaseline in my gasoline makin' grunts and noise like hoes doin' shows with erotic toys/in and out the glimmering alloys/shootin' the gap like my name was Frank
Zap-pa
cuz I'm a literary rap-pa/real Mother of Invention
need I mention
cab driving is a video game/frame after frame accelerating in the left lane/with right side of my brain
mad Coltrane/spinning off in psychic hydroplane
As I tunnel through the Caldicott

Flirt a little with women, Louisa May
Alcott
chick in the back says my rap is "tit-hot"
you can find me in the Alameda Tube with a Rubik's cube
head spinning in a bunker that rushes by
dirty walls and rods of light/whether you drive day or nite/watch out for rollerbladers jumping out of elevators skateboarders crouching below the sightline[15]
bicyclists that wanna manifest their eternal rest in pine
insanity and pain how do I define
a homeless madman peeing on a no-parking sign
pushing his cart out to meet Jesus
cop doin' what-ever-the-fuck he pleases
car door open in the corridor
I think I've had enough of this/garbage truck hauling ass like a wild rhinoceros down my esophagus
high speed stress like Keanu Reeves
in a full court press against Ali Baba and his forty thieves
cutting through lanes like fish veins
on Van Ness with the finesse of a sushi chef
Truly/defty/I'm the surfer with the motorcycle mentality/when it gets gnarly/I hit the slot between the herd and the Harley/tourist with his head in a map/kid on a raging Ducati/cab driving is how I rock a party

---

[15] I actually had a rollerblader (with the cranial capacity of a mosquito) grab onto the back of my six-passenger van cab so he could hitch a ride up the steep grade of Pine Street from Montgomery. I was talking to the guy sitting up front with me and found out only afterwards what happened. He took the first hill okay, but on the second steeper incline *dude* went flying and nearly landed under the wheels of a yellow cab racing uphill behind me. Thanks again, Saint Fiacre!

Cab driving is a video game/and it's this strict/red light runner in the red light district/in a white SUV blowin' one point two three/alcohol level through the roof/slammin' beers with bogus proof/I did this shit kid before you were born so back up you fake Tartuffe/
I'm headin' into the valley of death
but I don't quite know it yet/Civic Center sans seatbelt bolted down with a sort of pseudo concentration/left hand on the wheel yakkin' to my congregation
like it's the Hip-Hop Nation,
    yiggedy, yiggedy y'all
shadow streaking across a wall/skyscraper about to fall massive energy mashing six lanes/the moving mausoleum blowin' out brains soon there'll be flames/mind measuring the impact/it's a scientific fact do you see him? How fast can you react/headlights beam like spiritual antennae
heart racing like Bruce Jenner
sellin' Bo-flex
Tibetan Book of the Dead says dying is so complex
ego at a loss/body stiffening across/centrifugal force/headfirst like birth in reverse into the source
cops call it a T-bone/you call it the Big Bang that never was and zigzag away like rolling paper in a heart-pounding escape...
My name is M.C.Mars
I put out a record, a CD and a tape
Buy this book before it's too fuckin' late

Blood

7-28-88

"Blood was its Avatar and its seal..."
—THE MASQUE OF THE RED DEATH

Everything was a lesson that day, but I was so confused I couldn't get any of it straight. I couldn't even remember how I got there, walking around in the basement of a hospital with a box of frozen blood tucked under my arm.

"Anyone bingo[16] at the Blood Bank?" the dispatcher asked. "Turk/Masonic, who's for the blood?"

And here I was, at the end of another corridor heading for another cul de sac—dazed, distracted and loopy as hell. *"Where the fuck is the lab?"* I half yelled.

Last night, forty minutes of stolen sleep culminated in a nightmare—scene of carnage and chaos—plumes of fire, billows of black smoke, people covered in blood and ashes, crying out for help. I woke up screaming, too afraid to go back to sleep.

"Restricted Area" the sign in front of me read. I pushed on the bar. A set of heavy metal doors opened and slammed shut behind me. I understood the finality of the sound. The truth of it resonated in the depths of my life. Last night at sundown—or was it the night before?—I tested positive for HIV.

I pressed for the elevator and saw myself in its gleaming

---

[16]A "bingo" means a cabdriver is at the exact intersection the dispatcher is announcing. In this case, Turk Street and Masonic Avenue.

reflection, balancing the box of blood on my hip like a load of unwieldy schoolbooks. I stood there listening to the emptiness of the ventilation system, staring mindlessly at the foam-coated ducts and fluorescent lozenges in the ceiling. I kept telling myself I was gonna be all right. I was gonna get through this. Then I thought about T*** and the other women I had to tell. And another mad wave of fear descended upon me. I was caught in the riptide of an incurable disease, and the ramifications of this were becoming clearer every minute. So I did what I'd been doing all day, I prayed and mustered my faith and repeated the words, "Faith is to fear nothing, to stand unswayed, to surmount whatever the obstacle."[17]

When the elevator arrived, I got in chanting Nam-myoho-renge-kyo in a whisper under my breath. An orderly and an old man in a sky-blue smock laid out on a gurney with an I.V. in his arm accompanied me as far as level A, where the orderly held the elevator with his foot, pointed down the hall, and told me how to find the lab. Secure in the fact that I knew where I was going, I hit the nearest bathroom—not because nature called, but because I needed to cram myself into a small space and cry. I set the box down over the sink. It was wide enough not to fall in. I sat down on the toilet seat, but there was a loose bulb twitching overhead, which ruined the mood for the flood of tears I was expecting. I closed my eyes and bent forward, covering my face with my hands. I wondered how long I would stay sitting like this. My hands were cold from carrying the frozen blood and touching my fingertips to the roundness of my eyes felt good.

There were a few drivers I knew of who routinely got lost for an hour or more, picking up and dropping off fares with a box of

---

[17] From the poem "To My Young American Friends" by Daisaku Ikeda.

frozen blood in the front seat. I opened my eyes and looked at the box labeled St. Mary's, sitting astride the sink. Time's up, I told myself. The blood will thaw.

But when I got up I went straight to the mirror, pulled up my shirt and started examining the purple pimple I had discovered this morning just below my armpit, thinking maybe it was KS. *Karposi's sarcoma, opportunistic infection...*I knew the term in a very general sense from reading the newspaper. Up to this point, the most specific info I had on AIDS came via a thirty-minute video the clinic made us watch, prior to giving us the free anonymous testing.

Most poignant was a testimonial by this heroin-addict chick in a torn-up motorcycle jacket. Looking straight into the camera, she described her evolution from insane fear to the serene acceptance of death. At the end, flashing her photo and fatal parentheses, we learned she'd died of PCP (pneumocystis carinii pneumonia.)

Bone tired, I was glad to put the box down on the counter once I arrived at the lab. However, there was no one around to sign off and receive the blood.

"*Hello! Anyone home?*" I called out.

A new wave of anxiety hit me. I thought I'd fucked up the delivery. I stood around contemplating what to do next, when a female technician with a big smile came around the corner and thanked me so much for the blood. I never thought that anything as simple as another person smiling at me could be so uplifting.

Behind her I saw a familiar poster for *Bleachman*—the hypodermic needle personified as a blue-caped superhero. It was all part of a citywide campaign to stem the tide of AIDS by teaching junkies to clean their works with bleach. This *Bleachman* thing was all over town—in bus stops, on billboards—now here it was again, a marker in the prodigious upheaval of my life. Yeah, this was all a part of it, I thought bitterly, and returned to my cab, which had been parked indifferently at an angle—more or less blocking the ramp to the ER. Numbers (with the solemnity of tolling bells) kept jangling in my head 7-28-88/6:53. The key was still in the ignition.

For the next few hours, I drove around chanting away the fear loudly between rides. I was being extremely selective about whom I picked up, screening flags and radio orders for potential hassles. When I made a drop at Castro & Market, a respectable-looking woman in her late thirties asked me if I took dogs.

"I'm handicapped," she said. I looked at her and then at the little pooch on a blue leash. "Don't worry, he's very well behaved. He can sit on my lap." Once inside, the first thing she did was put the dog on the seat next to her. Given my weakened state, I told myself let it go. But then she told me to shut the radio off, because she was hard of hearing and the loud music bothered her. I thought this could use some clarification, but again—seeking to avoid any and all conflict—I decided not to make an issue of it.

"What kind of dog is that?" I asked in my friendliest voice.

"She's a cocker-poo."

"A what?"

"I said, she's a *cocker-poo!*"

I got stuck—midway through a turn at 18th & Castro—by a stream of humanity jaywalking en masse and a Muni bus, bearing down on me sadistically with loud and persistent honking.

"The trouble with San Francisco..." my passenger said, "is...very few people are cultivated."

"What?" I said, continuing to chant in a low voice.

"*What! What?*" she yelled.

"No, I agree. You're absolutely right...about what you were

just saying." I'm thinking, conserve energy. Keep the conversation to a minimum.

She was a speechwriter, she told me—the main speechwriter for Dianne Feinstein. "You probably won't believe this…" she said, and launched into this long résumé about how she's written grant proposals for the la-dee-da institute, and worked on such-and-such a committee, bla-bla-bla…Then she said, "Still, it's not easy being handicapped," and proceeded to tell me how she had punctured her eardrum. "I went scuba diving one day and the next day, I went skydiving. I still had water in my ear and at 22,000 feet, I felt it go pop!'"

"Ouch…," I said, forcing myself to be nice.

"Y'know why I'm going to Perry's?" she said.

"Why?"

"I'm going to settle a score with someone…I got kicked out of Perry's last night, because my hair was braided and my boyfriend is African-American. And then that asshole faggot, Michael the bartender, started giving me a hard time and ignoring my order for drinks—as if I couldn't buy and sell his skinny little ass twenty times over! You know what that prick said to me? He said I'm a nigger lover!"

"He actually said that?" I asked. "In 1988? In San Francisco?"

"Yes, that little twit. Can you believe it? He said that!"

And then I blew it. I really sunk my ship by saying, "If you're partially deaf, why do you have a *Seeing Eye Dog?*"

"This is not a seeing eye dog. This is a signal dog for the hearing impaired. You've probably never heard of such a thing, have you?"

Don't get into it with her, I told myself. It's too draining. In my hypersensitive state, I saw with new eyes how self-defeating anger could be.

"Never heard of a signal dog, huh, wise-ass? What's the matter, cat got your tongue? Hello, sir, I'm talking to you. I think you're the one with the hearing problem!"

"Madame, I'm not talking to you."

"Well, la-dee-da..."

"I have nothing more to say...So please..."

"Please, what?

"Shut up!"

"Why you rude sonofabitch!" she said, getting all red in the face. "Do you know how difficult it is to be handicapped?"

I felt like snapping back with a tale of my own, but what would be the point in that. She was Trouble with a capital T.

"You loser, you pathetic excuse for a man!" she yelled. "You probably drive a cab because you can't do anything else. You're probably in the closet! I know the type, takes it in the ass. Wanna suck dick, gay boy, you probably suck Michael's dick."

I wanted to laugh right in her face. But I couldn't. This was too bizarre. "You're a sick one, aren't you?" I said.

"No, you're the sick one, Mr. Rim-job."

We were closing in on the Hayes Valley playground, with its graffiti walls and bored-looking youth, hanging in front of the projects.

"Y'know, I'm tempted to drop you right here."

"And make me walk?"

"Yes, wouldn't that be nice?"

"Oh, wait and see. You're gonna pay for this. Your ass is grass."

"Lady, shut up! I don't wanna hear another fuckin' word out of your mouth."

"Well, tough titties..."

"Okay, now you messed up, big time..." I said, swerving the cab to the curb. "Get out!"

"Oh, like you have some kind of power to make me."

This was classic. When a guy refused to leave your cab, you had the option of giving him some help. But when it was a woman who refused to go, then what?

"I guess I'm going to have to call the cops," I said.

"Go ahead. And then I guess I'll have you hoist on your own petard."

I got on the horn to the dispatcher—more as a threatening tactic than anything else, since I already knew what he would say. He'd say the cops were going to be awhile—at least forty-five to an hour. Better to take her, save myself time and hassle. It was so busy on the radio I couldn't even get the dispatcher to read me. So I grabbed the microphone and, without holding down the button, I said, "Desoto 89, I'm at the intersection of Hayes and Webster. Send the police. I've got a crazy woman in my cab!"

"Is this how you treat a handicapped woman? Compassion isn't in your vocabulary, is it, pig?"

"Compassion *is* in my vocabulary and so is *lunatic!* Now if you don't want to get sucked through the exhaust pipe, shut up! I'm giving you another chance." And I proceeded to drive on toward our endpoint of Union Street.

"You verbally abused me. You threatened me. You sexually assaulted me...Hmmm, this will make a nice report..."

"I sexually assaulted you?"

"That's right, you cum-licking faggot."

"You're quite a case. Funny, in a sick way."

"Shut up. Say another word and I'll sic my dog on you. I give him the kill command in Spanish and he'll tear out the arteries in your neck."

I look at the six-pound Cocker-poo in the mirror.

"Now who's doing the threatening."

"That's right. I'll kill you..."

"I'm glad I have this all on tape. Thank you," I said, fidgeting with the radio as if it were in recording mode.

"Now you're really in trouble. It's against the law to tape without my consent."

"Tell that to the judge," I said. She cackled at this and said, "Boy, am I gonna enjoy watching you squirm..."

"Yeah, I'm really glad I recorded this..."

We were on Union Street by then—bars and restaurants and hi-end boutiques. Some folks were standing out in front of Perry's, laughing and carrying on. Soon as I pulled up, the automatic locks went down. I pointed to the meter and told her what she owed me. But she started going crazy, banging on her window, screaming to a group of people on the street, "Help, he sexually assaulted me..."

Alarmed and not knowing what to do, I opened the locks and she jumped out. So did I.

"You owe me for the fare!" I shouted.

"No, you owe me," she said. "I gave you a twenty and I want my change..."

The crowd was getting very interested in this. I was standing there speechless, shivering violently, looking around for some kind of—I don't know what—understanding? Rescue?

A waiter dashed out of Perry's and came running over to me. Starting to feel rattled, I said, "This woman is lying. I didn't touch her and she owes me money." I watched the woman and her dog cross the street and walk away.

"Good luck getting it," the waiter said. "She's not playing with a full deck. I eighty-sixed her last night. She's forbidden to ever set foot in here again." This guy was a godsend. "Hey, can you take another fare?"

"Sure," I said.

The couple he brought out were well-dressed, laughing, and apparently sane people. They warned me they weren't going far, only over the hill to North Beach. This was fine by me. Three minutes later, I said goodbye to them at the corner of Union & Columbus.

Though I wasn't particularly hungry, I knew I had to eat. More than anything, I wanted just to sit down and rest awhile. In an almost impossible piece of luck, I found a spot right on Columbus and grabbed it. Then I went into one of my favorite restaurants—a soulful place in the southern Italian style, run by the wives of garbage men—and ordered the veal parmigiana, half-pesto, half-vegetables.

"Half-pesto, half-vegetables, is extra," the waitress mused. "But for you, we make an exception." She smiled.

The moment she walked away, my eyes filled with hot tears, and I bit down hard on my lip to keep from weeping.

Moola Metaphysics, or the Bacon Booster

The word *fiduciary*—though it sounds like an Italian cussword—is a term associated with banking and literally means "founded on, or relating to, faith or trust."

When I turned HIV+ I got a lot stricter with myself in every way. In money matters, I became formidably fiduciary—and downright meticulous when it came to protecting other people's loot. For one thing, if I suspected someone had over-tipped me by even a dollar, I brought it to his or her attention immediately. Same thing with loose change on the seat. Also, when arrogant people stiffed me with a nickel or a quarter, I stopped throwing it back at them.[18]

I did this because I saw a clear connection between my continuing health and how righteously I dealt with the cavalcade of humanity pouring through the world of my cab. I was dealing with this illness not just physically, but metaphysically. In San Francisco, AIDS was killing people left and right. I figured my margin for screwing up was nil.

And of course, once I started living this way, large amounts of money—very large amounts of money not belonging to me—

[18] Particularly after some guy said to me, "What the fuck are you doing, asshole? That was a Susan B.!"

started falling into my hands—and all over my back seat—in ways that could only be called miraculous.

In the Winter of 1990, on the way back from SFO, I found $900 in my cab. There are few things more breathtakingly beautiful than the sun setting on the San Francisco Bay—except maybe $900 on the back seat of your cab. For me the appreciation of both came almost simultaneously.

Nearing Candlestick Point, with the bay rippling icy cold and the chemical sunset on the western hills blinding me with its furious meltdown, I thought I saw something unusual—unusually green—dancing around on the ceiling. I turned around and my jaw dropped! Nine crisp Benjis, hot off the press, lay fanned out on my backseat!!!

Right away, I knew the owner...The money belonged to a little Japanese lady, wearing an old raincoat and carrying a beat-up valise. I had picked her up in a cesspool stretch of the Tenderloin, where the drug dealers grind endlessly, using the little niches of basement doorways as makeshift urinals. A guy stood there emptying his bladder, half-turned to the street, a car length away from where I picked her up. This woman could not afford to take this hit. But me...Man, I wrestled with Temptation. Visions of all the plum things I could put this money toward danced in my head. I really struggled—almost succumbing to the magic effect of these bills—before deciding, "Fuck it! I can't do it. I'm returning the money!"

As I raced back to the United terminal, a little voice kept saying, *What a waste of time. She's probably on board right now, taxiing down the runaway!* But the voice was wrong. Risking a ticket, I parked out front and dashed inside. She was next-in-line at the ticket counter.

Excited and out of breath, I said, "M'am, please, check your money...I think you may have lost something."

She didn't understand. Her English wasn't good.

"Please, look inside your purse. Get your money out. Your money!!" With a cab driver yelling, "Your money..." in her face, she got scared and backed away.

Aware that I was going about this the wrong way, I calmed down, and said, "I found your money on the backseat of my cab." Watching her open her purse and poke around, I hoped like hell she would prove me wrong. But no, she started crying, making the plaintive little noises a puppy makes when it's been hurt. I quietly handed her the bills.

"Thank you *sooo* much...I can't believe I did..." She told me she lived in LA and had come up to San Francisco to borrow $900 from her mother, so she could pay her rent. She gave me *$200, as a reward!* I felt great—better by far than if I'd made off with the whole enchilada.

But getting such a generous reward may have set me up for future disappointment, because, a few months later, I nearly flipped when I walked into the Desoto Garage at about 6:45 one Saturday evening and found a long trail of money strewn tantalizingly at my feet! It had to be twenty feet long, from the gas pumps to the office—all fives, tens, and twenties. It was like a dream, the way I gobbled up that gelt. But again, I was pretty sure of its owner. The trail ended right at the door to the office. It belonged to a female driver who relieved the dispatcher, answering phones during his dinner break. This time, all I got was, "Thanks, man. Good karma..."

Okay, so not everyone has it in them to break you off a little *sumphen' sumphen'.* But the Bacon Booster—was another story entirely. The Bacon Booster was the kind of scruffy old degenerate chiseler nose-pickin' sonofabitch who'd drive a stake into the heart of a Good Samaritan, and walk away whistling. I picked this piece of work up one evening at 16th & Mission. He wanted to go to a homeless shelter at 5th & Bryant. As soon as he got in, he said, "Hey man, I hope you drive fast. They close the doors at eight, man." I looked at the digital clock. "We have fifteen minutes. No problem.

"Hey man, you do trades?" This is the kind of question guaranteed to instantly piss off a cabdriver.

"What are you talking about...diamonds, ground-up rhinoceros horn, cocaine...wha'da ya got to trade?"

"I got some delicious bacon, man. I'll give ya ten pounds of bacon for the cab ride, man. How 'bout it, man..." And then I noticed, that what at first glance appeared to be pizzas stacked across his chest, were in reality boxes of bacon—ten pounds of chemically treated bacon—all nasty orange and fatty white, glistening in plastic.

"That's a tempting offer. But what am I gonna do with ten pounds of bacon?"

"I don't know... Eat it. Have a party. Invite your friends, man. This is good bacon, man. The best. Top shelf, man."

"You mean, you took it off the top shelf."

"Hey, it's worth a five-dollar cab ride, man."

"Not in my book. And for your information, the exact fare will be closer to six dollars." He looked at me befuddled. And then he continued, "This is easily a twenty-five-dollar value—"

I cut him off. "Dude, show me the money or close the fucking door. This is a taxi, not a trading post." I looked at the bacon. It seemed to be sweating.

"Don't worry, man. I've got money, man. Money is no object," he said, slowly going through each pocket of his overalls.

"I'm glad to hear it...You have about thirty seconds to produce six dollars."

"This is quality merchandise, man. Valued at $25...It's a steal, man."

"Yeah, and you stole it. Now show me the money or close the fucking door! Okay, *man?*"

"Here it is, man! I got it, man," he whipped out a slightly wet, crumpled up bill. "I only got five bucks. Can ya take me for five, man?"

"Okay, but you have to promise me one thing. Promise me you won't say another fuckin' word to me the whole ride. Okay, man..."

"Yeah, man. No problem..."

In the eight minutes it took to get to the homeless shelter, this asshole must have said, "Five bucks, is that cool, man?" "Five bucks, is that cool, man?" "Five bucks, is that cool, man?" about ten times. After the first "I told you, yes," I decided he must be afflicted with some mild form of Tourette's Syndrome and I stopped reacting.

The fare came to five-ninety. I took the wet, crumpled-up bill and inserted it in the middle of my wad of fives, so I wouldn't have to touch it again until I absolutely had to.

"All right, have a nice night," I said, as he climbed out of the cab. He didn't say *thank you* or anything. He just got out.

"Hey..." I hollered out the window, "Why don't you do something for your fellow man...donate that bacon for breakfast!"

He gave me a look as if to say, *GET REAL...*

As I drove away, my interior light wouldn't shut off. He'd probably gotten the seatbelt stuck in the door. As I turned around to fix it, I was in Vegas all over again! I hit the jackpot—this time, to the tune of five-hundred-sixty-some-odd simoleons, scattered all over the back seat.

Now, anybody in his or her right mind would have said, "Fuck this guy. I'm calling it a night." But I was still under the spell of that Japanese lady and her $200 reward. So I went and gave the bacon booster back his bingo.

Inside the shelter, I told security I was a cab driver returning a lost item and the uniformed woman waved me through with no problem. I spotted him at the far end of the room, bedding down on a thin mat under some steam pipes. The place was pretty crowded. I had to be careful, walking through the maze of bodies. When I reached him, I crouched low and whispered, "Jesus may have turned water into wine...But you, sir, have turned a nasty five dollar bill into five hundred sixty bucks!"

On the down and low, I slipped him the loot.

He took it. And didn't say anything. No *thank you*—nothing! He just rolled over and showed me the bald spot at the back of his greasy head. Squatting there, I waited, and waited. Finally, the unrequited metaphysician in me said, "What, muthafucka? No reward!!?"

The bacon booster stonewalled me.

"So that's how it is, huh, man? Is that how it is, *man...*" I said. And walked away in disgust. At the door, I spotted some mean-looking hombres and walked over to them. "You see that bearded old fuck over there?" I said, pointing at the miser.

"He's your meal ticket. Tomorrow morning breakfast is on him. Ole Dr. Seuss over there has ten pounds of bacon and five hundred sixty green eggs stuffed in his coat pocket...Break the code, boys."

Then I walked out, trying to convince myself that I wasn't the stupidest bastard in the world.

CODA

The Gangplank in the Tenderloin was a long-time watering hole for tough-looking seamen and merchant marines. Now, under new ownership, it had transmuted into the gay version of longshoreman and stevedores. I went in, yelled "Taxi," and quickly retreated. Two guys, cobbled together in the doorway, staggered out. As usual, the guy least able to walk under his own power was the one who needed the cab. He was Oliver Hardy in rainbow suspenders, reeking of barley, malt and hops. He lived in the 500 block of Oak Street—a destination that was no more than a mile, a mile and a half away. We hadn't traveled more than a hundred meters when he started bellyaching.

"What the hell are you doin'? Why did you take Van Ness? I hate Van Ness."

"Well, how would I know you hate Van Ness, if you didn't tell me you hate Van Ness? I took this route because it's the fastest way."

"It is not the fastest way. Polk is faster."

"I beg to differ."

"Look at this, all damn these traffic lights. Well, there goes your tip."

"I'll live."

"This street is just pure aggravation. You're getting exactly what's on the meter and not a cent more."

"Fine." He wanted me to blow up. I wouldn't give him the satisfaction. No way was I gonna do that. But still, something slipped out. "As soon as you opened your mouth, I knew I wasn't getting a tip."

"Well, at least you're right about something."

Oliver Hardy popped his suspenders. Neither one of us said

another word until we reached his place. The meter read $5.10. He handed me five one-dollar bills and, before he could get too busy rummaging around in his pocket for the inevitable dime, I said, "Forget it. I'm giving you a tip."

"Well, actually you're not," he persnicketied. "Had you done it right and gone by way of Polk, it would have been $4.65...I know what it costs. I do this all the time."

"Would you like another dollar back?" I said waving the bill over my shoulder. But by then, he'd slammed the door and walked off. Straightening the bills out and attaching them to my roll, I noticed that, instead of five singles, he had given me four singles and a twenty. He was still within calling distance—huffing and puffing his way up the steps...

But I just couldn't do it. Calling out to tubby seemed like too much trouble, an unnecessary waste of breath, *too much moola metaphysics for me.*

MTV Writer Chick

"Why don't we ever know it when we need it?
No one says: Here's happiness weather."

—DIANA O'HEHIR

I'm sitting in front of a painted lady, honking—well, not exactly honking, something gentler than that: tooting. From inside the house comes a signal, lights flash off and on. It's pouring rain, coming down in buckets and cascading swiftly over the curb on the steep downhill side of Liberty between Dolores and Guerrero. A young woman with a see-thru umbrella comes out, sprinting toward the cab. Something about the way she holds the umbrella, the pure aesthetics of her flight, is extremely graceful, a ballet.

"You got in here faster than a hoe fleeing a pimp," I said, wincing immediately at the moronic statement.

She gave me a what-an-asshole look and handed me a piece of paper with an address on it. "I'm late. My friend's band is going on right now. So don't drive me all over town."

"Yeah, you got me pegged. That's what I do on a busy, rainy night."

"Hey, I don't know. You lean on the horn. You make a dumb remark. I just wanna get there fast, okay?" She was a beautiful girl, probably second-generation Korean with a touch of cosmetic surgery around the eyes.

"Sorry if I offended you."

"You didn't offend me. You just characterized yourself."

"Touché." I was really having a bad night. Way out of rhythm. I fell quiet, thinking about the spectacular collapse of my t-cells, news, as of yesterday. The implications and possibilities fucked with my head big time. Plus, the heat from the defroster had me sweating through my clothes.

"Hey, is that a camera?" she said, pointing at the intrusive red eye, poised above my rearview.

"Yeah, they just installed these. Smile for the dispatcher!"

"Really? Can he see me?"

"Nah, it's a digital camera. When you get in, it snaps a few pictures. They claim it's for our protection."

"It feels like *Taxi Cab Confessions.* Have you ever seen it?"

"No. But people tell me about it all the time."

"It's on HBO. You should see it. It's seems real," she paused. "You know how you can tell when people are faking?"

"Orgasms or television?"

"Both...It's a good show."

"It's mainly oriented toward sex, right? "

"Sex sells!" she ha-ha-ed.

"From what people tell me, the show sounds kind of contrived. People usually don't get in the cab and start spilling their guts or their bodily fluids...But then again, there are exceptions..."

"Really? Do people have sex in your cab?"

"All the time. This cab is a moving bordello. And that..." I said, pointing at the digital camera, "is really a webcam. You too can become an international porn star—just by taking off your clothes in my cab. Now..."

"No, really. I'm curious, because I've come close to having sex in a taxi myself."

"Sounds interesting. Tell me about it."

"There's nothing much to tell. I chickened out."

"Why? Whydja chick out?"

"You know, it's funny...I can't remember."

"A cop-out, if ever I heard one. I don't believe you."

"No, it's true. C'mon, tell me one of your best sex stories."

"In the cab? "

"Of course. That's what we're talking about."

"Okay, lemme set the stage. Do you want one where I'm the star or would you rather hear about other people?"

"Other people."

"I'm hurt."

"Have you had sex in the cab?" I felt like saying, Lady, allow me to introduce you to the harsh realities of life, and the harsher realities of HIV. I have a fever, bitch. I'm sweating thru my clothes. I'd just as soon Superglue my penis than have this conversation with you. But instead, I said, "I'll waive my Miranda rights. Yeah, I did."

"Where? In this cab?"

"Yeah. On the backseat, right where you're sitting."

This chick nearly hit her head on the ceiling, screaming, "Here! You had sex, here. Here! On this seat!"

"No, not there. On the other side. Stay where you are, you'll be fine."

"Tell me you're joking."

"Yeah, of course I am. Anyway, here's a story. And don't worry, it didn't take place in this cab. The year was 1992. The place, *Big Heart City,* it's a night club. You know it?"

"No, but I'm not from around here."

"I never would have guessed...Anyway, it doesn't matter... Two couples get in. Glam rockers. Big hair. Leather jackets, the whole nine. Just like tonight, it's raining cats and dogs. They wanna smoke a doobie. I say okay, no biggie. They pass it around.

The guys are laughing, speaking Dutch. The women are kissing and fondling each other, which they have been doing since they got in. By the time we reach the Cathedral Hill Hotel everybody's stoned and the chicks are going at it hot and heavy. The windows are opaque from smoke and body heat. I kill the engine in the carport and watch, along with my comrades. One chick goes down on the other. Legs are flying every which way. A boot heel hits me in the ear. The Dutchmen roar. And everyone lives happily ever after. Like the story? "

"Yeah. It's pretty hot."

We turn left from Valencia onto 16th. The police have cordoned off the area between the *Skylark* and the *Esta Noche* with yellow tape. An ambulance is screaming in our direction.

"Something's happening," she says.

"Yeah," I say. "Something's always happening."

"And it never stops."

"What never stops?"

"The something that's always happening...God..."

"Wow, that's profound."

"Not really. It's mostly bullshit."

"I'll buy that...Here, pick a number. Your number, please." I push a flimsy plastic bag under her nose, the kind you get at the supermarket for fruit. The bag is filled with thirty scraps of paper. Each one is folded over and has a number written on it.[19]

"What's this all about?"

"Just draw out a single scrap of paper."

"What do I get if I win?"

---

[19] I was actually conducting a little experiment—letting my passengers choose the order of my stories as they would appear in this book by picking them out at random. A method I have since scrapped.

"Nothing. It's a study in statistics. I'm working on it with six other Nobel prize winners at Livermore Labs."

"Oh, so I'm taking part in a very important experiment."

"Exactly." The situation in the cab is so make-believe—truth and fiction are often the same thing. The deeper reality, and the more complex *truth,* lie in the emotional connection we make.

"I just had my Tarot cards read," she says. "Very interesting. My cards were rife with hearts..."

"Rife?" I said.

"Yeah. I'm a writer..." she said, proudly.

"You'd have to be. Who else would use the word *rife*."

"I know. I can't help myself. When I was a waitress, the other servers use to laugh at me because I'd say things like, 'The salmon comes in permutations,' instead of saying, we serve it in different ways. Or, we have 'onomatopoeia onions' instead of saying frizzled onions. *Onomatopoeia* is when a word sounds like what it means."

"I know," I said. "I'm a poet." But this never registered. She kept right on talking.

"This guy in the band, I only met him last week. I'm kind of nervous about meeting his friends."

"You—and all those guys? What's to be nervous about?"

"I mean his girl friends. Guys are a pushover. Girls are tough. They're so critical. And I'm a girl's girl!"

"Sexually speaking?" I ask.

"Sometimes, yeah. But I just like girlie stuff, you know... Talking about guys, make-up, that kind of thing..."

"You're from LA, right?"

"Howja guess?"

"Call it cab driver's intuition. Do you write screenplays?"

"No, I write for TV."

"Which show? "

"Let's just say it's the worst show on MTV."

"How did you get the job? I'm always curious how people manage to make these career leaps."

"I took a course at USC extension. My teacher worked on the show and brought me on. My Big Break! Six months ago, I was a miserable waitress going nowhere. Now I'm a writer!"

"How old are you?" I asked, painfully aware that I was passing familiar signposts down the road to numbing Depression.

"Twenty-five. How long have you been driving a cab?"

"Twenty years and some change."

"Twenty years, wow! That's incredible. I was in kindergarten when you started driving a cab..."

The doctor says I have to go on meds. If I don't, I'll probably die in two years. Meds scare the hell out of me. I managed to stay off them from my diagnosis in '88 till now, the year 2000. I don't think I would have lived this long if I'd started on AZT back then. And now, somewhere in the back of my mind, I equate going on meds with death by meticulous poisoning. We arrived at the club. The rain slowed to a drizzle. She gave me a twenty.

"I'm a writer too," I heard myself saying again, as I gave her change. But she didn't care. She was already waving at someone, leaping excitedly out of the cab, dodging puddles.

*"Cast a cold eye on life, on death, horseman pass by...*That's Yeats!!" I shouted out the window. But she was gone. Out of range. Kissing someone under the canopy, as if they were both on top of a wedding cake.

Super Geriatric Antediluvian Funk

According to Buddhism, *The Four Sufferings* of life are: birth, death, sickness and old age. Buddhism never mentions taxes. Or Jewish mothers. Or little kids in the ghetto throwing rocks at your cab as you roll through. But, for me, the most frightening suffering to contemplate is getting old on a fixed income in the inner city. I once picked up a seventy-year-old man at a good hospital. When the security guard wheeled his chair down ramp toward me, I had to keep myself from firing up the engine and taking off. Like it or not, the expression on his face said, *the next forty minutes belongs to me.* He wore a standard smock, and had no slippers on his raw scabby feet. As I helped him into the cab I noticed a dagger tattoo on his flaccid forearm. "Where are your shoes?" I asked. He had none. He smelled of beer and urine and mumbled his speech. He told me his emergency monitor went off and when the paramedics came and dragged him away they didn't take his shoes or even the keys to his apartment. All he had was a voucher from the hospital to pay me, and a plastic bag with some medicine inside. That is how the hospital released him. When we got to his building, we tried four or five of his neighbors on the intercom but no one would buzz him in. Of the two people who answered, neither knew who he was. Finally, I flagged down a Sheriff's deputy and left the old man in his custody standing barefoot on the cold sidewalk.

Besides the everyday dangers they face in the streets, seniors are sometimes held prisoner in their own homes. Drug addicts and dealers and burglars attack at will. They break into mailboxes, stash boxes, and *lunch boxes.* They steal Social Security checks, money, medications, baloney sandwiches—anything they can lay their hands on.

A nurse from the ER at SF General once told me about an eighty-year-old woman they brought in kicking and screaming, after she had been beaten and raped. Seniors living in rundown hotels spend their entire day alone in a tiny room, watching TV. And, of course, these are poor people we're talking about. The rich live in the splendor of palatial retirement homes, dine in fine restaurants and frequent the opera. I don't think they've ever been cursed out by a shopkeeper, the way I once saw a shopkeeper curse out an old woman—barely strong enough to carry her bag of groceries—for holding up his line. If she had had clout, he wouldn't be working there anymore.

In the cab, seniors (rich and poor) all agree on one thing. "Don't get old," they warn you, without offering an alternative. "Never get old," they say as they struggle against stiff limbs to leave the cab. Every now and then, some guy with wattles and lighter fluid in his veins will say something poetic like, "*Always go to a bar where you're known. Always take a cab home.*" Or, "*It ain't much of a tip, but it's better than a poke in the eye with a sharp stick.*" But the notion—put in my head long, long ago—that wisdom comes with age—is certainly a crock of warm excrement.

"Who can pick up Jean?" the dispatcher pleaded, pitching her to the drivers. "Long-time Desoto customer. Lives in the Panhandle. She's a really, really sweet lady…"

It was Sunday night, a little after 10:00 P.M. I took the call at Mel's Diner on Lombard. An old lady in a purple beret, waving a pink scarf, flagged me down. When I stopped, she said, "Hi, I'm Jean. I called. Are you for us?"

"Yes, I am," I said.

"Excellent," said Jean, with a smile. Then she turned and went to the curb, where an even older old lady moved stiffly under her guidance into the cab. "Eunice, give me your hand, dear…Watch your head…" Jean said, as she lowered Eunice in. Eunice's face was half-hidden under a wool cap. She had on a hospital bracelet and her skin was translucent.

"That's my Desoto," Eunice squeaked. "We only use Desoto!"

Driving south up the steep side of Divisadero, the bay windows burned brightly in the mansions and embassies of Pacific Heights.

"How was dinner?" I asked the ladies.

"Fine," Jean said. "I had a roast beef sandwich. And the French fried potatoes that came with it were delicious." (She didn't cheapen them by calling them "fries" or "French fries.")

"I had a hot dog," Eunice grumbled. "I didn't care for it."

"What was wrong with your hot dog?" I asked. The wizened old lady made a face, and said, "It tasted like rubber and it was just plain lousy."

"You should be eating roast beef, like your friend here," I said.

"Yeah," Jean said. "You should be eating roast beef, like me…"

"Well, it's very late and I can barely eat anyway, so I decided to have a hot dog," Eunice said. "I've always liked hot dogs, ever since I was a little girl."

"You can't be a day over sixty-five," I said, joshing.

She started clucking with laughter. "Holy Hannah, are you

ever wrong! I'm going to be ninety next month!"

"How can that be?" I said. "You must have the fountain of youth in your bathtub."

"I don't think I've used my bathtub in twenty years, except to wash some clothes."

"Well, it's true," Jean chimed in. "She looks great for her age."

"God willing, I'll live to see the New....Men-ill-ium" Eunice giggled, knowing she had mispronounced the word.

"That's not how you say it..." Jean laughed. But she couldn't get it either, calling it the "new Men-noon-ium."

"No, it's the new linoleum..." I said, which sent the ladies into stitches.

"The new man-ill-ium? Ah, that's not it either," Jean sighed.

"It's harder to get than a greased pig," Eunice said.

"The new mausoleum, the new man-hole-ium...the new millennium. That's it, *The New Millennium,*" I shouted victoriously, and stopped the cab. This I thought to be an appropriate pause, a chance for the ladies to catch their breath, they were both laughing so hard.

"Why are you stopping? I don't live here," Eunice said, turning ice cold.

"I know, I know...," I said. "I did it for dramatic effect."

"What in *botheration...*You better just get your foot on that gas pedal and drive this car. That meter's running and we're trying to get home," Eunice commanded.

"He's only playing...," Jean said.

"I don't care about any of that malarky. You keep driving till you get to the 1700 block of Grove at Central. Then stop."

"Okay, okay...," I said. "Your wish is my command."

"What a nice cab driver...," Jean said.

"He's not nice. He just wants a tip. That's all."

"Sooo...Eunice...," I said, "I'm sure you're gonna live to see the New Millennium. It's only two months away."

"What's the other name for it? " Jean said.

"I'm not sure. You mean the new linoleum?"

"Don't start that again. Please..."

"Y2K...Is that what you mean?"

"That's right," Jean said. "*Y2K.* Did you know that, Eunice?"

"What-ever-you-call-it...That's when Jesus is comin' back..." Eunice said, passionately.

"Are you sure about that?" I asked.

"I'm sure."

"Why are you so sure?"

"I heard it in church. We're gonna have Canaan Land," Eunice testified.

"Caning land—like in Singapore, where they hit bad people with a stick?"

"No, no—Canaan Land..." Eunice corrected. "The promised land. All this is gonna be gone, wiped out, *destroyed!*"

"Why do you wanna live to see everything destroyed?" I asked.

"Well, *I don't care. I'm goin' to Heaven!*" Eunice yelled.

"What about the rest of us?"

"Don't you think it's a little late to be askin' that now, mister? I can tell you this—and I got it straight from prophecy—all the sinners are gonna burn up in Armageddon hellfire."

"And you wanna live to see it..."

"You betcha, mister. I wanna be there when the Lord comes back with a sword of fire."

"But all that death and destruction—doesn't that go against the principle of *love thy neighbor*?"

"Not when it's God's will..."

"But what about the newborn babies and all the innocent

children…Do you wanna see them 'burn up' too?"

"If it's God's will, we have no say in the matter." I looked in the mirror at both ladies. Eunice was aiming her index finger at me. Jean shook her head as if to say, not every Christian thinks that way.

As we pulled up in front of her building, I asked her, "How do you spell *Eunice?*"

"What do you care?" She demanded. "Why are you writing my name down…?" I shut off the engine, and got out and went around to the door to help Eunice. Jean told Eunice to sit still while she freed a ring of keys, held by a safety pin to the outside of Eunice's dirty brown coat.

"I'm writing it down…cuz…I'm gonna write a story about you."

"Look here, Mister, don't gimme any guff. And don't go writin' my name down on that piece of paper."

"Okay, whatever you say. But it's a shame. *Eunice* is a beautiful name."

She made a sourpuss face. "You oughta sell snake oil. I take Desoto Cab all the time. I've never had anyone write my name down before."

"Well, I crossed it out. Now, may I help you to your door?" I reached down to help her and she pushed my arm away .

"Let the cab driver help you, dear," Jean said, waving goodbye. "And Eunice, remember we're having lunch together this Tuesday…"

The old matriarch grumbled.

"Let him help you, dear. He just wants to help you…"

To the degree that she would let me, I helped Eunice to her feet. I put my hands under her shoulder blades and guided her frail frame to the entrance. Chinese menus with footprints on them littered the doorway. Others were fanned out thickly in the door-grille, like a deck of playing cards. "This city is getting dirtier and dirtier by the day, and I don't like it one bit!" Eunice said.

"Blame the mayor."

"Ah, fiddlesticks!" She said sounding disgusted. "He's comin'... Don't that frighten you?"

"Who, Willie Brown?"

"No. The Lord of Hosts!"

"No, it doesn't frighten me. Not at all."

"Well then, mister, I feel sorry for you. Cuz you're in for a heap of hurt!" She shook her head, tightened her lips, and ignored me—waiting for the elevator to come.

When I got back in the cab, Jean said, "They don't make 'em like that anymore. She's something else, that Eunice..."

"Jean, how do you spell *Eunice*?"

Making It with My Muse

This is how I found the elusive woman of my dreams. And how she treated me well, and gave me light and healing when there was nothing but darkness—this mystic city, reaching back centuries, to the opium dens of Chinatown and the palm trees of the Mission Dolores. This is the story of how I fell deeply in love with her, simply by driving her streets and traveling alone with her at night through moments of shimmering beauty. How I discovered her naked subtleties, her nooks and crannies (warts and all) looking down alleyways, or at snapshot vistas forever etched in my memory. And how I found my coat-of-arms in her streets—my Fleur de Lys, my emblazoned lion—in the noble pattern of a manhole cover.

Found escutcheons and shields in cement vaults belonging to PG&E, in trapdoors leading down into storage cellars, gratings, sewers, drains, air vents, statuary standpipes with elegant little chains dangling between spigots. Found supreme beauty in a domed synagogue patched with verdigris and in the bronze doors of Grace Cathedral. Found love in the late afternoon shadows of a Crocker-Amazon playground, where *Free Mumia* posters peel off walls, and in the yachts, sleeping at night in the marinas of Crissy Field and Sausalito...

San Francisco...

You give me "picture-this" visions of love for every day I spend here...In shapes, and shadows, and shudderings of passing clouds; in flights of pigeons over fire escapes; in the circles and trapezoids and towering spikes of dazzling architecture—I have decoded your diary of symbols and dead-end lives. I have entered deeply into your secrets, and fought on your streets, and walked across your seven square miles stoned. And, more than once, I have stood in awe, looking south from Marin at your clay-red bridge, lost under a boa of clouds, your immaculate towers bleaching like fabled minarets in the angular sun.

San Francisco, painted lascivious of ladies, I sing to you of racing wheels and last-minute lust...5:00 A.M. shot to the airport...pedal to the metal in the dawn light on the high fluid ramps of SFO. *Yo*, with my mouth hanging open like a cab-door, and my eyes fixed on your pulsing Transamerica ruby, I weep out loud for the glory, and the power...And the fact, that after twenty fucking years on this dead-end job, I never put my name on the list to be an owner!!!!![20]

---

[20]In San Francisco, you become a medallion holder (i.e., an "owner") by plunking down a few hundred bucks and signing your name to a long list of other aspiring hopefuls. This list is monitored and supervised under the aegis of the SFPD. Then, ten or fifteen or twenty years later, whenever your name happens to come up for eligibility—resulting from the city increasing the number of cabs—and/or, the death(s) of existing owners—you receive notice of this financial bonanza in the mail. And from that day forward you are never quite the same.

Tienes la Roca

For Ron Bosia

3:52 A.M. Monday

My first ride, after an hour of orbiting the downtown, was at a low-rent Taj Mahal with the word "tandoori" splashed across its dome. It had a heavy wooden door and a large aquarium-like window swimming in darkness. I banged on the door and shouted, "TAXI!!" Then I pressed up close to the glass and hooded my eyes against the street-glare to get a better look.

Nothing. Nobody there.

I went back inside the cab and reported this to the dispatcher. "Wait," he said. "It's a fresh order."

Outside, it was wet and windy and vaporously cold. I honked. When nothing happened, I dashed into the cold again and tapped my keys against the window. "Taxi! Taxi!" This time a light came on. In my end-of-the-night delirium, I found myself studying the laminated menu posted on the door, as if it were a document of great import—the Preamble to the Constitution, a speech by Nelson Mandela, Martin Luther's 95 chutneys. I then announced to the great emptiness around me, *"FUCK THIS!"* and dove back into the warm cocoon of my cab.

The instant I turned on the ignition, two employees came rushing out—a Filipino guy, mid-to-late 30s, in checkered chef's pants, and a young woman, in her early 20s with a serious shelf.

She wiggled across the seat. Her name was Sheila. She was going to 25th & Shotwell. He was going to San Bruno and Bayshore. The cook was chomping on some watermelon-gum.

"Bro, I'm tellin' you—this young tender is a porn star. She was molesting me back there."

"In your dreams, Cecelio..."

"Straight-up Vanessa Del Rio shit."

"Cecelio..."

"Cecelio..." he mimicked. She hit him playfully on the shoulder. "Cecelio, you are so crazy."

I was hauling ass down Mission Street pumping Rick James. The loud music insulated us against the 4:00 A.M. emptiness. The nightclubs and the bars and the gated liquor stores had all gone to sleep.

"She's a super freak

Super freak

Super freaky... Yowww..."

Cecelio was singing and bouncing around in the back, pointing at Sheila during each chorus.

I taxi-mamboed around a homeless sheik wheeling his shopping cart down the center of the street and eluded a person of indeterminate gender with hair the color of tar, waving at any cab (or car) that passed. "Stop! I have a medical emergency..." she yelled.

"I bet you do," Cecelio laughed.

At the light, a Yellow Cab pulled up behind me. She bum-rushed him. But as soon as she grabbed the door, the driver had second thoughts and gunned it, leaving her in the middle of the street howling, "Eat shit and die, faggot!!!"

Sheila lived between two streets named after poets—Dante and Virgil. Her building was tagged with gang graffiti. "Hold up a minute, bro. I'm gonna walk the lady to the door..."

"That's okay, Cecelio...I'm fine."

"I know you are, baby. That's why I wanna walk you to the door."

"Bye, Cecelio..." she slipped gracefully past him, winking and blowing a seductive kiss.

"Hey, Wild Thing..." Cecilio calls after her. "Ima holla at you later on...Be ready for my call."

Back in the cab, he announced, "I ain't got nothin' to prove. I ain't some young punk out here *flossin*."

"San Bruno and Bayshore, right?"

"Yeah, get off at Silver..." I jumped on Cesar Chavez heading south.

"These young broads, man...These young broads will play you for your last dime, if you let them. But my game is too tight to get hosed down like that."

"Uh-huh..."

"I'm a gentleman, you feel me. A real man treats a lady with respect."

"Uh-huh..."

"*Straight playa,* you can't lose that. It's in my genes. But I ain't about to jump baby's bones in no taxi. I got too much class for that. You feel me..."

"What was goin' on in the restaurant? I was waiting a long time."

"Man, shorty is freak...But, nah, I ain't gonna do her like that. I ain't about to disrespect on her." I made the turn at the Silver and got off at San Bruno.

"When I was incarcerated I had a lot of time to think about

women. Man, that's all I thought about. You know what I'm sayin'…All the bullshit I pulled—callin' 'em bitches and hoes, treatin' my baby's momma like garbage. A woman is a goddess. If you can't appreciate a goddess, you can't appreciate shit. You feel me…"

"I do."

"Like James Brown says," the cook started singing, "'It's a man's world, but it would be nothin' without a woman or a girl.'"

"Yop…"

"Think of your mother…That's what I try to teach these young punks out here. I try to put a jewel in their skull. But these knuckleheads, they don't listen. They all caught up in they game, gettin' they bling-bling on, and shit and shit. But really it's all about respect." He sang it: "R-E-S-P-E-C-T."

"'Find out what it means to me.'"

"I ain't no Captain Save-a-Hoe, dawg. Fuck that. I work too hard for my shit. But you know what, cousin, I understand women. I know their needs. Act like you into her even when you're not, and give her flowers on her birthday."

"They love flowers."

"They eat that shit up, bro. You feel me."

"Uh-huh…"

We were almost at his place when he said, "Oh shit… We gotta go back."

"Back downtown?"

"Yeah, I forgot my damn keys. They with my homie."

"We're almost at your place."

"I know. I know, bro, but we gotta go back. My homeboy—got my keys."

"Listen," I said. "My shift is almost over. I don't want to get hit with a late charge."

"Don't worry. You ain't getting' hit no late charge. Go to Van Ness and Market. Trust me, dawg…I got your back."

"If I'm late one minute (I tend to emphasize this) they're gonna fine me fifty bucks. Are you prepared to cover that? "

"I take good care of my cabbies." He handed me a twenty. "Trust me, bro. Hold that."

I hotfooted North on 101 and closed in on Van Ness and Market like a heat-seeking missile.

When we made the scene, I did a little loop. He was craning his neck out the window, periscoping this way and that, studying the dark corner with the big A&M carpet sign, which, to his transforming gaze, must've read, "Crack Central." In the bus stop, a sales force of Mexicans were chillin'. Buses came and went. These guys stayed. Nothing could be more obvious.

"Go around the block," the cook commands. I did another lap. No luck. "Where the fuck is my boy? Shheeiit…" He opened his window and spit out his gum.

"Now what?" I asked.

"Just drive around for a few minutes. If I don't see him, we're gone." I drove down Van Ness to the glass rotunda of Davies Symphony Hall, several hours earlier glittering with the pomp and circumstance of silk gowns and penguin suits, and then I boomeranged back. At the corner of Market and Van Ness, by the doughnut shop, he said, "Stop. I think I see him…"

I twisted around and saw a guy in a 49ers jersey, leaning against a cyclone fence. The fence was decorated with clothing and all sorts of battered, miscellaneous crap—a midnight garage sale that never sleeps.

"Don't go nowhere. Ima be right back." I watched him bolt across the street and almost get run over by the 91 Night Owl. Then I parked on the opposite corner, by the Volvo showroom, engine running.

I heard him holler, "*Tienes la roca...*" And saw a few guys take off jogging, as if he were a leper bringing untold harm upon their community. Other dealers turned up their palms and walked away shaking their heads. He got back in the cab.

"Shit. I don't know what's up with these Mexicans tonight."

"Yeah, well...I gotta get back."

As I was about to close the book on this saga, he started screaming, *TIENES LA ROCA, TIENES LA ROCA...*as loud as a religious nut with a bullhorn. I turned around and saw the cook hanging out the window, sucking on an imaginary glass-pipe, as if he were playing charades. "*TIENES LA ROCA...TIENES LA ROCA...*"

Anyone within two blocks could hear this imbecile. I told him to quiet down but he ignored me. A young drug dealer, the object of his attention, stood fixed to the spot, absolutely horrified at what he was seeing. And what he was seeing, if I read the look on his face correctly, was major jail time. He was seeing a helicopter swoop down, and agents from DEA/FBI/ATF/IMS/CIA slamming him facedown on the sidewalk in a rabid search for drugs, each agency exacting its own brand of torture as they tore him limb from limb. But when this didn't happen, the young dealer came bounding up to the cab with his finger to his lips, giving the international *ssshhush-ut-the fuck-up* sign, and jumped in the back.

The cook mumbled to him, as if the transaction were suddenly a big secret. After they made the hand-off, the young dealer jumped out and disappeared into the cold night.

"I'm taking you home now. I have no time for anything else." He nodded his agreement.

"As soon as I get back to the crib, I'm callin' Shorty up and tappin' that ass."

I turned up the radio and flew.

"Yo, bro, can I smoke a rock in your cab?"

"Sure. Why not?" I said, making my sarcasm obvious.

"I'm just fuckin' with you, man... You got a cellphone? I'll call you next time I need a cab."

"No, I don't have a cellphone." I was running out of time. I hit the curvy, downhill shot from San Bruno to Bayshore at about 45 mph. "Yeah, you drive like me." The cook beamed.

"Where?" I said. "Stop...where?"

"There." He pointed into the dark at something I couldn't see.

"You said San Bruno and Bayshore. We're here."

"Make a right on Sunnydale."

"You said—" I slowed to a crawl.

"Don't worry, man. I'm gonna take care of you... Trust me."

His voice had turned flat and mechanical. I started to tense up. The muscles in my neck tightened. We started down Sunnydale, past where the old Geneva Towers used to stand. I remember watching the implosion on TV, the last high-rise housing project in San Francisco—the way it collapsed and fell in on itself. An evil structure, it released a spectacular cloud of poison gas and dust. I also knew a driver who'd been murdered there years ago, an English bloke with an incredible record collection.

We were on Kelloch, a little side street.

"Stop here," the cook commanded. It was dim, nobody around.

"I gave you twenty, right?"

"You did."

"Here's another one," he said, handing me a second twenty-dollar bill.

I looked at him. The meter read $33 bucks.

He smiled, and then said, "No. That's not enough." He slapped another ten on my shoulder and pumped his fist in the air. "That's a $17 tip. That's how we do, Filipino style."

And with an arch pimp stroll, a kind of "Super Fly" remnant from the '70s—the cook with the checkered pants cranked up his broken-leg walk and dipped off into the swirling mist.

The stars and celebrities (not including athletes) I have had in my cab are:

Alistair Cooke
Buddy Guy
Karl Malden
Screamin' Jay Hawkins
Tom Brokaw
Ike Turner
Patti Smith
Dennis Farina
Pat Reilly
Delroy Lindo
Lily Tomlin

But my favorite was George Clinton,
who technically was not in my cab.
He was in my friend's cab.
The distinction will be made clear in the next story.

Droppin' Mad Flava with George

For Buzz Brooks

Cold/rainy/4:50 A.M....

I was gassing up at the Olympia station at Cesar Chavez and South Van Ness, standing in the semi-dry perimeter of a dripping overhang. A driver I knew, a musician, on his way home in his Toyota truck, honked at me from across the street and swooped up to the gas pumps. "You'll never guess who I had in the cab tonight!"

"Who?" I replied.

Buzz took out a pocketsize tape recorder, pressed play and reached his arm toward my ear.

"Recognize the voice?"

I didn't.

"It's George-mutha-ship-Clinton!"

He had picked him up in the Castro at his manager's place. "At first I didn't realize it was George, but once I did, I dropped some flava..." Buzz whistled a few note-perfect bars of "*One Nation Under A Groove.*"

"Guess he liked my whistling, 'cuz he gave me his number at the studio and told me to stop by after the shift."

"Ya gonna call him?"

"I don't know. You think he was serious?"

"Absolutely...If George Clinton says 'call,' he means it." We stood in a light drizzle and hit the pay phone on the edge of the premises. "Hello, is George there?" Buzz focused his eyes on the pay phone. I watched him. The person on the other end wanted to know who was calling.

"This is the cab driver who took him over to the studio earlier. He invited me to come by after work."

When Buzz said the *cab driver*, I cringed, "Don't say you're the cab driver..." I whispered. "They'll hang up on us."

After years of experience I'd learned, when trying to make a favorable impression on somebody, never start the conversation with the words "*I'm a cab driver.*" It invites rejection. I expected them to hang up immediately. But to my amazement, the enlightened party on the other end must have said, "Hold on..."

"What's going on?" I buzzed in Buzz's ear.

He put his hand over the grimy receiver. "It's the security guy at the studio. He's trying to locate Nina, George's manager."

I tried coaching. "Yo, tell him you're Buzz, the musician/singer. When you say cab driver—"

Buzz motioned me to shut up. The person on the other end must have said, "The cab driver?" Because Buzz said, "Yeah, the cab driver."

Then Nina, or whoever it was, must have said, "Oh, the cab driver. Yeah, sure, come by..." Because when Buzz hung up, he gave me a big smile and a *pound*,[21] and said, "Let's go see George."

The session was taking place at Hyde Street Studio on Hyde between Eddy & Turk in the heart of the Tenderloin, where the symbols of human degradation are loud, bold and shameless. At 5:25 in the morning, the wet streets were dark and quiet. A soft drizzle continued to fall in windswept veils under the streetlights. A prostitute, indifferent to the weather, squatted between parked

[21] He tapped his fist on top of mine and vice versa to complete the cycle.

cars to urinate. Parking was nowhere to be found. Anything that looked like a spot was in *7:00 A.M. tow-away zone.*

Buzz said, "Shit, I don't know how much longer I can drive around."

"We'll find something...Just keep circling."

And a few minutes later, we nailed one. As we approached the studio with its intentionally nondescript exterior, a truck loaded with equipment was pulling away. Buzz said, "Damn, looks like we missed 'em."

"Screw it. We're here. Let's ring."

Buzz needed a catalyst, someone to get him past the improbability of this. I was only too glad to help. Buzz punched in the code. We stood around waiting, huddled against the outer door which had no ledge to shield us against the rain, getting wet and wetter, until a metallic voice said, "Who's there?"

"It's the cab driver," Buzz said.

"Why do you have to keep saying that?"

Before he could answer, we were buzzed in. As we crossed the threshold, Rastaman at the door yelled, "The cab driver is here! The cab driver is here!" The greeting rang out, and was picked up by other voices echoing down the corridors of the studio. "The cab driver is here, the cab driver is here!"

Short of throwing flowers at our feet and garlanding our brows with laurel leaves, they escorted us with great fuss and fanfare—like the true street ambassadors we are—directly into the room of rooms, the inner sanctum of George.

In the center of the room, directly behind the engineer, a guitar player with an exhausted look on his face sat with an ax on his lap. Behind him in a chair sat the inimitable Doctor Funkenstein, holding a furry little mutt named Atomic Dawg.

"George! Whuz happenin'!" Buzz boomed.

George waved, and said something low and garbled and friendly—multi-colored dreadlocks bunched like astral asparagus on top of his head. He was patiently coaching the guitar player, teaching him a lick in four parts, which to save his life, the dejected musician couldn't get. George hummed it for him over the track. He did this many times in a row, like a truly unruffled mentor, without losing patience.

Meanwhile, Buzz was buzzing, chafing at the bit, leaning into me and whispering, "Wish there was a keyboard around. I don't see one." Then Buzz started humming the lick too, advising the guitar player on the key—which obviously, by the look on his face, he didn't wanna hear. Suddenly, everyone started putting in his or her two cents—even the guitar player's sexy girlfriend, who had been sitting there enduring all in silence, sharing the same glum expression as her man. She started humming too. Soon everyone in the room was humming in the poor guy's face except me, and Matt, the engineer. He was trying to get levels. I was free-style rapping in Buzz's ear.

The guitar player in a display of overt disgust with himself dropped his ax, dropped his head, and asked for a break. Buzz said to George, "My buddy, Mars, here is a rapper." George pulled out his pipe, took a vicious hit. While sucking down oodles of gray-matter-depleting smoke, he gave us a quick series of smiling nods. Luckily, I had a CD with me. I had intended to sell it to a driver that day but hadn't, because we never made the connection. I handed my *Street Opera CD* to the maestro.

"Mmmm..." George said, turning over the jewel box and looking at the artwork on both sides, smoke streaming out of his mouth. "I'm gonna listen to it." Then he took another vicious hit of synthy, intergalactic, mojo pebbles—and exhaled a second serious blast of smoke.

Around 7:30 A.M., Buzz did a stand-up stretch and yawn routine and said, "I gotta go. My girlfriend's gonna throw a fit."

Twenty minutes later, George and company called it quits. They were red-eyed, cranky and cabin-fevered—having been in the same room since the previous afternoon, laying tracks. On the console was a *DAT* tape earmarked for the Oakland rapper *Too $hort.* I was tempted to ask about it, but Matt was still working with careful concentration at the board. With the track looping, I started improvising again.

Matt said, "You're a rapper."

I said yeah, and did an a cappella version of my song, "Days of The Outlaw."

Matt said, "Spit that verse for George." We found George in the hallway. Standing near an upholstered bench along the wall, I go—

I drive a cab in the city by the B-aaay
Danger is the way I earn my pay
I drive a cab in the city by the B-aaay
Danger is the way I earn my pay
These are the days of the outlaw
Never knowin' what you're in for
Days of the outlaw
Never knowin' what you're in for

I drive hard on the boulevard/graveyard
Shift/skyline insignia illuminati
2 decades hackin'n' mackin' in Frisco City
keepin' shoes on the baby while I practice my artistry
stuck in a stark reality
hustler on the/periphery/of society

ya never heard of me/the M-A-R-S emcee
deep in the igneous
underground recognition is slight
so I write/keep a diary at night
catchin' thrills/on these breakneck hills
on and on to the Bay Area dawn
bustin' nuts/crazy/like I starred in porn
or war-torn Kosovo/so act like you know
and don't compare me to no "midnight cabbie "
cuz I'm real/and he ain't never been stabbed see
I'm the emcee floatin' in the think tank on the Left Bank
of the Westside taxi who-ride
on the horns of a dilemma
like the Dalai Lama/in the land of the snake
I don't fake rhymes/cleasin' my Karma for these millennial times/
breaker one-two I got my foot in the door/been here before/and I'm still smokin' mari-ju-ana
one eye scannin' for the po-po
the other fixed on the street piranha
every point I make/every rhyme I spit/is true life drama

When I finished George laughed his approval, and repeated my line, *I drive a cab in the city by the B-aaay*...Then he says, "Come back tomorrow, I wanna record that."

I went home too excited to sleep. I called my sister in NY and told her, "You're not gonna believe this, but tomorrow I'm recording a song with George Clinton!"

"Who's George Clinton?" she said.

Next night, I showed up ready to go, books of lyrics in my bag. Dreadlock security let me in. Dap-dap, I was inside and gliding upstairs.

"Yo, Mars!" Matt greeted me. "I don't think we're gonna have time for you tonight. George wants a mix of the three songs we did yesterday, and I'm mad pressed for time. He's gotta catch a 7:00 A.M. flight. Sorry."

Emptiness, disappointment, rejection—why let old ghosts plague me? why trip?—it had been too bizarre to shake out any other way.

"If you want, hang out..." the engineer said.

So I did, listening quietly to three *phat* tracks. About a half-hour later, a voice from downstairs announced, "George is here."

"Go downstairs and talk to him." Matt said.

Down in the kitchen, George was scratching around, looking for food like a big, hungry bear. In the cabinets above the sink, he found some crackers and a box of baking soda. In the fridge, he found a jumbo bottle of Pepsi, half-full, and a bowl of humus. He began scooping and scarfing, hammering down soda in large gulps. He pulled an empty baby food jar out of a lower cabinet.

"I ain't slept since Friday," George said, pouring boiling water into the small jar and mixing the recipe—of this and that, a variation on the theme of protein powder and baking soda—to produce more of his favorite delectation.

"Been filmin' a video all afternoon with these fools up in Hunter's Point. There's a war goin' on up there." He described sitting in a truck with these guys who are armed to the teeth—trying to make a video and kill their neighbor at the same time. He said it was ridiculous. The video equipment was hot and no one knew how to shoot a video—or a gun. He laughed and mimed aiming a gun with his face turned the other way. "This is how they shoot. Muthafuckas couldn't hit the broadside of a barn!" He shook the jar gently until the contents cohered into a sticky mass, then he finger-molded a rock from the new batch and fired it up. He sucked the smoke deep into his lungs and spread the nefarious smell between us.

While George smoked, I spread out my lyrics on the counter top. While George riffed about assassinations and conspiracies, and how the FBI and Interpol routinely pose as Crips and Bloods to stir shit up—I looked for an opening where I could introduce my lyrics. When he stopped to scoop the last remaining bit from the bottom of the bowl, he held the *Wheat Thin* and the glass pipe in the same hand, never daring to release the pipe from his tight grip.

I read him a poem about a man and a woman having a libidinous romp in front of a mirror at sunset. He hooted with laughter and looked over at his security guy. "We'll use that one on the website!"

I felt the stirrings of hope, a resurrection in the sepulcher of my heart, where I thought to have buried forever my musical ambitions. I followed George out of the kitchen into a small room with leather sofas at opposite ends. We sat facing each other. By this time, I wasn't counting, but George must have taken 25 to 30 blasts—each little rock a strange visitation, a brief encounter with Nirvana. And while he was seeing elephant-headed gods and heavily ornamented goddesses with eyeballs embedded in their palms reclining on orange lotus flowers and blue-bodied voluptuaries levitating in Tantric flight—*makadociously*[22]—he said, "You're not addicted, unless you think you are."

Then he started talking about the Internet and what it will be like living in a virtual future, where there is no Time because Time will have collapsed in on itself like a super-nova, or an intergalactic mojo pebble going up in smoke. I was in awe of the

[22](măk·ȧ·dō·SHŭs·lē) Origin: Ebonics/hip-hop dialect/SF/Oakland Bay Area /mid-90s/c.f. Latin "pimptaurian."

way this man was formulating these things with the clear mind of a Buddha lost in Alice's Wonderland and thought, This is great, even if we never get around to recording. But then an intern, an assistant-to-the-assistant engineer, showed up and said, "Go upstairs. They're ready."

In the recording room, I had them dim the lights. And I adjusted the highly sensitive and very expensive microphone, with its little round screen called a pee-popper to protect it from plosive sprays. When the beat came on, George wanted me to rap in a style that was "real laid back." I did, and then went on and on, for about twenty minutes of free style. When it was over and I came back inside, George stood up and embraced me. "I'm gonna use it on the record." Nina had me write down my social security number for their accountant in LA. George said he was flying to Tallahassee on family business, but he'd be back mid-week.

"When I get back, let's hang out and have some fun..." he said.

I couldn't believe it. I couldn't have written a better script. One of the people in the console room was a Veteran's cab driver Nina had brought along as her guest. He stood leaning against the wall, petting and scratching the head of Atomic Dawg. "It didn't take you long to whip him into shape!" he said to George.

"He was already in shape when I met him," George replied.

"George," I asked, "why are you so kind to cab drivers? It's like you have a *Let's Adopt a Cab Driver Program.*"

He looked at me like I was simple, and said, "Did you ever try to find a cab in this town? It's hard as hell. Imagine what it's like for a big black man with a dog."

He couldn't have been more pragmatic. And I couldn't have been more unrealistic, in clinging to the hope that this might go somewhere.

The Envelope

Oppenheimer 40, La Rocca 20, Gordon 20, Santiago 20, Nakamura 20...
It is a treasure I will always keep. An 8.5 x 11 manila envelope consisting of forty-two names, the names of cab drivers, listed in three different styles of penmanship, by three different cashiers, over a period of three weeks. Red, green, black and blue are the colors of the ink.

Jane Bolig 20, Tassie 20, Paulsen 20, Molyneoux 20, Bob Miller 20.
The envelope stood posted in a bulletproof window four inches thick. Behind it, the cashier handed out medallions and waybills and took money at Desoto Taxi, my employer for twenty years. The company had moved to a new location but nothing had really changed. Under harsh fluorescent light—the dispatcher and the order taker worked in front of a computer and multi-line phone with their headsets on. Our new home was a Quonset hut in a fenced-in compound, on a one-time condemned piece of land, on a street often glittering with broken glass, a haven for homeless encampments and fugitives living in dilapidated RVs, running pirate generators off the City's power.

Tom Williams 10, Cydear 20, Canright 20, Panther 5, Bryak 10, Scoble 20.
At the top of the envelope, the flap cum heading read:

Driver/Marchal Silver, St. Mary's Hospital Rm #755/ Acute Pneumonia.
Little did they know that "acute" was my euphemism for PCP. On December 11, 2001, after running a fever of 105°, I capitulated to the vehement insistence of friends and had myself admitted to the hospital.

Edwinson 10, Dudley 20, Regan 10, Hunsaker (aka Big J) 20, Andy S. 20, Wickham 20, Guinshard 20, Cameron 15…
By the time they brought me in, it felt like I had a dumpster sitting on my chest. I could hardly breathe.

When my buddy Roscoe drove me to the hospital, he said, "What's that black shit on your face?"

I looked in the mirror of his van. I had two black lines running down my cheekbones to my jaw line from lack of oxygen. Still, I hated the thought of going to the hospital and proposed making a pit stop at Burger King instead, as a sort of last minute compromise, so we could weigh the pros and cons of this drastic decision over fries. Roscoe wasn't hearing it.

Neither was the intake nurse. "You're really sick."

Then, she pulled out this little machine and had me stick my finger in this clothespin-like contraption that measures your oxygen absorption rate. Mine was seventy-three. After I was admitted and friends came by, I'd have each of them stick their finger in the machine and take a reading. Everybody was up at ninety-eight, ninety-nine, even the chain smokers. Seventy-three is a few coughs away from dead.

Winz 10, Brooks 10, Gilbert 21, Mehrdad 20, Tubwell 10, Brinkerhoff 10, Papakostas 20…

Then, about two weeks after I left the hospital to start my recuperation, I had an outbreak of shingles—a type of herpes virus—all over my face. It wasn't pretty and, it hurt, the way bad bruises hurt.

Carolan 10, Sudki 20, McNevin 20,Gillespe 20, Gallagher 10…

The year before, I had almost died from an allergic reaction to my meds. In between episodes, I'd had a basal cell cancer removed from my forehead, which seemed like a reprieve.

Coryell 20, Houseman 20, Wai 10, Snowden 10, Greg Cochran 10…

They collected six hundred and ninety-one bucks, money I desperately needed to subsist off until my food stamps and four hundred dollars a month from the City kicked in. Only two guys knew—the one who brought me the money, and the other one, who killed and dispelled rumors bruited around the gas pump by the occasional busybody.

"I never heard of pneumonia lasting three months. He must be pretty sick. How'd he get it?"

"Sitting on a dirty toilet seat…Running in the rain…I don't know. When he comes back, ask him."

"He must be in a bubble."

"Blow me with your bubble."

"Seriously…"

"Seriously."

Cab Driving is a Noble Profession

Out by Ocean Beach, a kid came sprinting down the street, yelling and screaming obscenities like an exorcised spirit, begging me to help him. Behind him, closing fast in the fog, I saw a gang equipped with bats and chains. I said, "Get in!" and we jetted.

At the corner of Bush & Larkin, I broke up a robbery in progress—two thugs, attacking an old man with groceries. I drove up, flashed my cab badge and screamed, *"POLICE! FREEZE!"* They took off running.

In the Lower Haight, I discovered a discarded Xmas tree on fire—an apparent act of arson—and stomped it out myself before the trucks arrived. For a cab driver, this is part and parcel of the job. Any cab driver who's been driving as long as I have will have similar stories—some, a lot better than these. The point being, cab drivers, in their most ideal and exalted capacities, function as true public servants and protectors of the people. From providing useful information and helping folks with directions, to the aforementioned dramas, to the simple act of making sure passengers *get there safely*—cab driving is a noble profession.

I mean, think about it. We turn our backs on strangers every day. What a ballsy gesture, turning your back to a stranger—

particularly in America. What a supreme act of faith, what a fragile bridge of love—what a bond of respect and trust the cab driver proffers his public. I ask you, who—besides high-wire artists, orange-vested highway workers, mountain climbers lost in a blizzard, graveyard gas-station attendants and convenience store clerks—who is more susceptible to violent mischance than a cab driver?

Cops carry guns and routinely call for backup before putting themselves in harm's way. We live out our dramas alone, unarmed, in dark and desolate places. To say that the cab driver puts his neck on the line is not enough. To a criminal, he's a paycheck on wheels. His head must look as tempting as a piñata.

That's why I tell the young dude with the tool belt I pick up at 4:00 A.M. on a sketchy stretch of lower Polk, "Put the tools in the back..." And as I finger the tire iron I keep by my side like a medieval weapon for tearing off faces, I say, "You can ride up front with me."

When I say cab driving is a noble profession, I think of all the drivers killed in robberies or by deranged assholes for the thrill of it. I think of Lucy, the Brazilian lady driver who got beaten up by hookers in the bathroom of the Desoto garage and left a trail of blood fifteen yards long. Or that mulatto woman who always wore a 'Niners jacket and got jacked by punks for being a dyke. I think of Italian Cal from the Mission who smelled forever of Irish Spring soap, who had an accident, lost his job, and not knowing what else to do, blew his brains out. I think of all the people in all the cities around the world, shot in the back of the head, or shot in the back through the seat, or the ones who had their throats slit, all because they needed to go out and make a living.

And I think of Cole Johnson, my friend for a short time, the up-and-coming actor/musician/Yellow driver/who got out to ring a doorbell in the Mission in the bleak of night, and got clocked upside the head by punks with a two-by-four. Cole spent five years in a coma before dying and leaving behind a wife and infant.

Then, I think of myself...Walking along the underbrush of the highway toward the overpass, dark, plum-colored blood trickling through my fingers, worrying about my lack of medical insurance. Worrying about what I was going to do next—stumbling over an occasional rock along the path, as the dazzling afterglow of my survival swirled brightly around me.

In the firehouse at Ocean & Phelan where I found refuge, I sat down and told my story. Someone handed me a paper cup. I drank the cold water.

"I can't believe it," the female firefighter said. "You look so calm!"

"I'm glad you can't read my mind."

Several other firefighters entered the room. She told them the story, leaving the punch line to me, "Please drive, motherfucka, you're gonna kill us both!"

I got the laugh I was looking for, but I felt fake and dizzy, a sleepwalker in a land of hi-resolution pathos. The paramedics came in. They put an oxygen mask over my face. With latex gloves, they cleaned and bandaged the wound. I heard the cadence of my breathing, the first cause, the primal sound that human beings make when all else is silent.

I studied the faces in the room. A man was still mulling over my story, looking thoughtfully at the bloodstain on my pants. A mixture of respect and wonder, tenderness and healing, showed in the eyes of everyone in the room. These people, who didn't know me from Adam, seemed to care about me, a cab driver who'd gotten stabbed doing his job. I needed their love. I sipped and savored it like expensive champagne. But would they still feel the same way, extending themselves with such natural, open concern, if they knew I was HIV+? When they handed me a questionnaire to fill out, I decided not to check the box for HIV. They were professionals. They were using gloves.

The cops arrived. A sergeant with an Italian last name asked me for a statement. I regurgitated the story. She jotted down the facts in her little pad. Then she handed me a slip of paper with her name and case number on it and said, "I'm glad you're still alive."

"Thank you," I said. "So am I."

Acknowledgments

In 1998, when I started writing these stories, my octogenarian friend, the writer Mel Fiske, gave me tremendous encouragement and support by reading and critiquing the early drafts. Now, almost seven years removed, and at least 30 drafts later, I thank you from the bottom of my heart, Mel. I also wish to praise the memory of my two great teachers, José Garcia Villa and William Ball, to whom this book is dedicated. José, with his superb taste and aesthetic discipline, helped me form my ideas about poetry. And Bill—with his scholarships and grants to the American Conservatory Theatre, which he co-founded—always shined a light on me. "Keep writing," he would say. "Keep writing." Nothing could have been more important to a young writer than to have a man of his stature take such an interest and give me this kind of unqualified support. Also, I want to praise the memory of another great teacher, Stewart Brady, "a dignified man of stained-glass beauty."

But "*Don't Take Me the Long Way*" would never have gone from a manuscript to a finished product without these people. Big ups and huge props go out to Donna Beech, an amazing editor (and one of the smartest women it is my pleasure to know) for her humor and penetrating insight in the form of 321 pinpoint comments. To Cesar Puentes at CP Design for his straight-up doper than dope graphics. To D-Ray Archer for her generous contribution of a great photoshoot. To Patty Holden, for her expertise as a typesetter, and her eleventh-hour wizardry and instant friendship. To Frank Herrera at *Showcase* magazine, for giving me a shot with the "Taxi Literati" column. (Frank, I couldn't have gotten this far without your help.) To the staff at *Showcase*—big ups to Kay, Will, and Jelani. More thanks to Tim

Murphy and David Thorpe at *POZ* magazine, and to Walter for cuttin' me those checks, and to everybody I've dealt with on staff at *POZ*, stay strong.

Also, heaps of gratitude go: to Gabriela Maltz Larkin and John Hunsaker for answering the phone late at night, and listening patiently while I read them slightly different versions of the same stories ad nauseam. To Dan Poynter, for giving me a road map through the jungle of self-publishing. To Gordon Burdgett, for critiquing my book in its penultimate stage, and suggesting that I include an introduction. To the remarkably talented Kieron Dwyer, for the M.C. Mars logo, the Off D Edge Press logo, and the mcmars.net website. To Mark Kaplan for helping me get Off D Edge Press off the ground. To Nico da Silva for my business card on short notice. To George Clinton, for his magnanimity in letting me publish an uncensored version of "Droppin' Mad Flava..." and the sheer joy of letting me climb aboard the Muthaship for a hot second. To Matt Kelley at Hyde Street Studios—for havin' my back! To Isaac "Big I" Frierson, for teaching me to forget that I was fucking up and just freestyle. To Deejay Lymus, for the beats in the cab. To Dr. Dorothy McQuown, for keeping me alive when I didn't want to be. To Dr. Ken Mills and Joan Brosnan, R.N., for keeping me alive now that I do want to be. To Jon Janes for his friendship and big-time legal advice. To Flo Selfman for her generous contribution of a proof reading. To RVS for the mail order coupon, hugs and kisses. To Dorothy Wall for her early editing back in 2000. To Sandra Yeyati at Whitehall, for her interest in my project. To Gary Archer, and to Buzz Brooks (the Brookstore!), *good lookin' out, yo.* And, to the Desoto drivers whose names appear on the envelope, what can I say? You're the best.

Finally I want to thank my friends and family for sticking by me through it all, especially my mom and my sister, Randy.

PHOTO: D-RAY ARCHER

About the Author

M.C. Mars is a poet who lives in San Francisco. Early in his career, he studied privately for a year in New York City with José Garcia Villa, the protégé of e.e. cummings. He also resides in a parallel life, where he is perpetually a five-year-old boy being raised by wolves.